THE LAST ALIAS

THE LAST ALIAS

True stories and a tale that might be.

STE7EN FOSTER

Seven Wonders Press

Paperback ISBN: 978-1-7356035-1-3
Hardcover ISBN: 978-1-7356035-2-0
EPUB ISBN: 978-1-7356035-3-7
KINDLE ISBN: 978-1-7356035-0-6
Audio ISBN: 978-1-7356035-4-4

Published by Seven Wonders Press 2020
New York, New York USA

Some names and identifying details have been changed to protect privacy. Certain events have been combined and conversations edited for narrative clarity.

Cover Concepts & Design by Ste7en Foster
Photography by Michele Grinstead
Makeup by Wendy Martin
Book Design by Brent Spears

For the Magnificent Seven:

Dale, Jim, Mona, Mom, Dad, Stephanie, and Fred

“I’m on the path to being someone I’m equally terrified by and obsessed with. My true self.”

—Troye Sivan

Contents

A PREFACE

THIS BOOK WAS WRITTEN PRE-COVID.

Is this a bad time for a book about finding your true self?

Maybe. We're looking for so many other, possibly more important things right now.

I wrote the book because I thought my story—these stories—might help somebody. And if I helped even just one person, everything I went through, well, it wouldn't have been worth it, but it will make the fact that I did much easier to swallow.

We are feeling a little lost in all this.

So who's to say? Maybe it's the perfect time for this book.

But I guess you'll be the judge of that.

INTRODUCTION

MY NAME IS STE7EN FOSTER.

Who are you?

Yes, you can answer with your name, of course. Or your occupation if you are, like so many of us, identified by your profession. But who are you really?

I guess a better question is, *Which* are you really?

Because we're not really just one person, are we? We're actually many. A collection of constructs created—consciously or subconsciously—to make up the representations of You that you show to the world. It's not a new concept that we all wear masks to some extent. Philosophers and thinkers and pundits have pondered and debated the question of one self versus many for centuries.

For example, you're not the same You to your best friend as you are to your boss. And your best friend probably gets a different You than your spouse does. It's not a bad thing. It's not like you're lying to all these various people. You *are* these different persons. Or personas. Which one is the Real You?

I'm asking, not because I'm in a more self-aware state than you. I'm not claiming any psychological superiority by any means. In fact, I'd wager that I'm far behind most of you reading this.

Because I don't know who I am.

I thought I did once. But after a series of, as Lemony Snicket would call them, unfortunate events, I lost sight of who I was. These events were so life-changing, I wondered if I ever even knew myself at all. I certainly don't know who I am now.

But I want to find out.

Naturally, I look online for some program to help me. Besides a lot of think pieces on the concept and nature of self, the only thing I come across are retreat-type excursions. Most of them involve a remote desert or mountain location, a severe diet that makes vegan look like a splurge, days of silence, and a yogi, or master, or *someone* in a bathrobe. Every program is exorbitantly expensive (those robes don't come cheap, I guess) and the Yelp reviews vary widely, from "this place saved my life" to "these flakes are a bunch of con artists." I think maybe I can come up with something on my own.

Admittedly, these are pretty airy fairy concepts to begin with—persona, the self, identity. For me to grasp them, I feel I need some sort of material representation. Something symbolic. Something I can put my hands on. So I land on an idea that seems pretty solid to me. Maybe even inspired.

First, I'll need a bowl. This whole experiment (for lack of a better word) is important to me, so I don't want to use just any old battered mixing bowl I have in my kitchen. I want a container specifically for this purpose. I know exactly the kind I want—small and round at the base, then it bows out and comes back in, leaving a wide open mouth at the top. I find something exactly like this on, of course, Amazon.

Now that I have my bowl, I take slips of paper and, on each one, I write the name of one of my personas, or "selves." I fold up each one and place them all into the bowl. I'll descend (ascend?) to a meditative place, as much of a thoughtful mindspace as I can. I'm not going to go hoodoo voodoo crazy. I won't light candles or burn incense. I won't wear hemp and have sitar music playing in the background. There are no rules. I'm making this up as I go along. I have no idea if it's going to work or not. I'm just following my instincts. I'll just be, using the buzzword of our time, *mindful.*

Then, one by one, I'll extract the pieces of paper and consider each self carefully. I'm hoping this ritual will help give form to the formless. The bowl—my mind, my soul, whatever you want to call it—will then be empty of all the other selves and I'll just meditate quietly on what remains. I believe what remains will be my true self, and that in this meditative, reflective space, it will be revealed to me. I'm not looking to have any religious vision or anything like that. But I think this process will lead me to a deeper understanding. Maybe even a personal revelation.

You're coming on this experimental little journey with me.

But let me give you a heads-up about the "Me"s you're going to meet. Not all these people are pleasant to be around. Some selves I don't like at all. Some I'm very comfortable with. Some are hard to admit are actually there. Most are fairly entertaining. Others, enlightening. Some might take a while to find. Others, I'm sure, I'll be able to locate fairly easily.

These various selves, they're like aliases I use. I rely on them. I need them. They help me react to and relate to my environment. They're not these carefully designed assumed identities, really. No more than you "put up a front" when you're being a Son or Daughter. That would imply there's more of a calculation going on here that's almost deceptive. These selves just *are.* They simply *exist.* I may or may not have had a hand in designing them, but they're not meticulously planned constructions. These selves are all me but they're not all *of* me. And I'm not looking to banish them. I'm just wanting to put them aside for a time. Fortunately, they all come with their own story, so they're all easy to identify.

Some stories will be from my adolescence, my young adult years. I happen to be one of those people who glean much of my identity from what I do, so there are stories from both my time in advertising as well as ones from my sixteen-year career in anime. A few stories will be from a time of illness.

If you're merely looking to read a few good stories, hopefully, this book will serve that purpose. All the tales are true except one—and even that one I think is pretty spot-on. As usual with these kinds of things, some names have been changed and events shortened or combined for better narrative clarity.

Look, maybe you're not like me. Maybe you know yourself like the back of your hand and you don't have to go through something like this. If you do (have to go through something like this) and you don't (know yourself as well as you think you should), then maybe my journey will help you with yours. Perhaps you'll see glimpses of yourself in some of these "Me"s. Maybe by reading my stories, you'll be able to understand—or tell—*your* story a little better.

It'd be nice to think that all this blood, sweat, and tears isn't just for my benefit. Not all these stories are fun to tell. But I feel I have to tell them if I'm going to be truly honest about this whole adventure. These are my selves. I have to own up to them.

You're a brave soul for coming along. Thanks for doing so.

I'll see you on the other side.

I reach into the bowl and grab the first piece of paper…

THE BONE TREES

The Survivor

i am six years old (the devil's number) and my cousin takes me out to these woods near his house and he makes me take down my pants and he tries to stick his dick in me and then he wants me to do the same to him but i am younger and shorter than him so i can't do it and then he gets mad and he hits me and pushes me to the ground and he leaves me there and the big leaves are scratching my naked butt and i am all alone around these tall gray trees that are really skinny, more like bones than trees, and i finally stop crying and pull up my pants and find my way back to his house where my mom is and she wants to know why i didn't come home when he did and that he said dogs chased us and we got separated and i nod yes, dogs separated us, and those dogs separated me from a world that day and those dogs have been keeping me out ever since.

NEITHER SNOW NOR RAIN NOR HEAT NOR GLOOM OF NIGHT

The Son

THE QUESTION IS POSED BY MY FATHER, WHO IS SEATED IN HIS recliner, his face hidden behind the pages of the day's newspaper. I should have been prepared for this, I suppose. I am, after all, almost eighteen and this is about the time when such things should have already been decided, probably.

"What are you going to do with your life, son?"

The question startles me. Not because of the question per se, but more because of the person asking it. My father doesn't talk to me very much—so little that when he does, it's somewhat startling. The question isn't snide, nor is it some kind of setup. My father isn't a calculating or cruel man. I know my father loves me. I just think he doesn't like me very much. We're just two very different people. But what teenager doesn't feel almost evolutionarily different than their parents? My mother and I are closer, but I'd still say her comprehension of me is somewhat limited. I look at her now, in her pink-tiled kitchen preparing dinner, glancing my way, slightly concerned that an answer is so slow in coming.

In the end, I choose the only thing I know how to do, the thing I have been doing since I found my mother's Smith Corona typewriter in the bottom of a closet when I was seven years old.

"I'm going to be a writer," I say with shaky confidence.

The newspaper doesn't move. I never do see his face. Is he… disappointed? I've disappointed my parents so many times before. I am not the son they always thought they'd have. I am difficult. Oppositional. Moody. Like any teenager, I guess. But still, more than they bargained for, more than two moony-eyed teenagers dreamt of when they got married. I am different. From them. From everyone.

I sense my confidence slowly leaking from me. I can *feel* myself deflating. All that's missing is a rubber wheezing sound effect. My mother, ever the optimist, finally says something, breaking the silence, coming up with what seems a practical application for what to them seems like such a nebulous, perhaps dubious skill.

"Well, you could always work for the post office," she says.

I am a little thrown by this, the logic of it eluding me for a moment. I don't see the correlation. Encouragement on her face and in her voice, she connects the dots for me.

"They send letters."

THE PENGUIN

The Freak Of Nature

FADE IN:

EXT. HEAVEN

We're in a blue, cloud-filled heaven. On the throne sits GOD in all his flowing-hair regality. God seems very proud of Himself. Before Him stands his squat subject.

This is THE PENGUIN.

He's pristine, as if freshly popped off the assembly line.

PENGUIN
Hi there!

GOD
How ya doin'?

Penguin's immediately thrown by how casual God is.

PENGUIN
No complaints.
(animated once more)
Okay, spill. What am I? What can I do?

GOD
You, my not-quite-feathered friend, are a bird.

Penguin is gleeful.

PENGUIN
A bird?!?! Awesome!

Penguin flaps his arms excitedly but sees long-winged appendages that resemble oars more than elegant wings. The flapping slows down considerably as he sees what he's working with.

PENGUIN
Uh, when do I reach flying age?

GOD
Oh, you don't fly.

PENGUIN
Don't or can't?

GOD
Can't.

PENGUIN
Oh. Bummer.
(catching himself)
No offense.

GOD
None taken. I get that a lot.

PENGUIN
What? Disappointed birds?

GOD
Disappointment in general.

PENGUIN
Well, as a bird you kinda expect flight to be just part of the deal, ya know? Wouldn't think a bird would have to spring for the extras package for something like flying since that's what birds do. Mostly.

GOD
Ah! Flying birds are old hat. With you I've done something special! You may not be able to fly but…

God pauses teasingly.

Penguin waits for God to get to the point.

PENGUIN
(slightly unnerved)
What?

GOD
…you can swim!

Penguin is beside himself.

PENGUIN
Shut up!

GOD
You shut up!

PENGUIN
I can swim?

GOD
Like Phelps.

Penguin starts jumping up and down, flapping his arms once again, now with renewed vigor.

PENGUIN
That's awesome! Where's the pool? I gotta try out these fins!

GOD
Wings.

Penguin immediately stops jumping.

PENGUIN
Huh?

GOD
They're wings.

PENGUIN
I thought I was a fish.

GOD
No. Where would you get that idea?

PENGUIN
From the fact you told me I could swim.

GOD
You can.

PENGUIN
Fish swim.

GOD
True, they can. So can you.

PENGUIN
But I'm not a fish?

GOD
No fish.

PENGUIN
No fish.

GOD
But you eat fish.

PENGUIN
Wha?

GOD
That's your favorite food.

PENGUIN
No, that's cannibalism.

GOD
No it isn't.

PENGUIN
How not?

GOD
Because you're a bird.

PENGUIN
Oh now you're just fuckin' with me.

GOD
Swear to Me. Not fuckin' with you.

PENGUIN
(polite but frustrated)
Grrr. Hold up. So I can't fly but I can swim.

GOD
Correct.

PENGUIN
I can swim but I can't fly.

GOD
Bingo. But, basically, you just switched those around. You're saying the same thing.

PENGUIN
JUST GIMME A MINUTE!
(correcting, putting his rage back in check)
I am so sorry.

GOD
We're good.

PENGUIN
You sure?

GOD
Solid as a rock.

PENGUIN
Okay, sweet, back to point. I'm a bird that can't fly.

GOD
Yes.

PENGUIN
I'm a flightless fish.

GOD
Yes. I mean, no. All fish are flightless except that one bugger where I got the bats too close to the carp and, well, it was a mess I'll just leave it at that.

PENGUIN
I can imagine. Everything working okay in the shop the day I was cranked out?

GOD
Like clockwork. One day and no reportable workplace accident.

PENGUIN
Well that's a comfort.

GOD
Still our longest record.

PENGUIN
Wow. Okay, I'm not a flightless fish so much as I'm a swimming not-fish.

Now they're both just being pissy.

GOD
I don't know if I'd put that kind of a spin on it.

PENGUIN
Well, You're not me.

GOD
Not saying I was you.

PENGUIN
I mean I just wouldn't go up to You…

GOD
I thought you'd be happy with things.

PENGUIN
…and tell you how to describe Yourself.

GOD
It's like you'd almost prefer worms.

PENGUIN
Not askin' for worms here.

GOD
Then what is it you want? Me! So ungrateful.

PENGUIN
If I'm giving the impression I'm ungrateful I'm sorry. I'm just…

GOD
What? You're just what?

PENGUIN
Confused.

GOD
You mean difficult.

PENGUIN
Difficult? What the fuck, difficult! What am I? I'm a bird but I can't fly. I'm not a fish but I can swim. I have wings that are more like Olympic rowing oars. I could poke somebody's eye out with this mouth you gave me, I have no legs…

GOD
Now he wants legs.

PENGUIN
Like it's too much to ask!

GOD
Are you finished?

PENGUIN
And on top of all that I'm fat.

GOD
That's not my fault.

PENGUIN
It's mine?

GOD
You could do cardio.

PENGUIN
Without legs?

GOD
Swimming. I *said* swimming!

PENGUIN
It looks like You just shoved two feet right onto my stomach.

GOD
There's just no pleasing you.

PENGUIN
Superglued two size nines. Pop! Bam!

GOD
None of you.

PENGUIN
Right there. Stomach. Shoes. Stomach shoes. Stoes.

GOD
Oh now just stop it!

PENGUIN
You stop it!

GOD
You haven't even looked in the mirror.

PENGUIN
Like I'd want to!

GOD
It's just rude.

PENGUIN
Is it?

GOD
You'd be singing a different tune if you did.

PENGUIN
Would I really?

The Penguin shakes his head, clears his throat.

GOD
Don't.

Penguin opens his beak and brays.

PENGUIN
Honk!

GOD
Ingrate.

PENGUIN
Well, isn't that a pleasant sound? Now it makes sense why you'd give me the ability to swim. Not a lotta concerts held in the deep blue, are there?

GOD
I wouldn't call that singing.

PENGUIN
Neither would I! There's hardly a word for the orgy of aural pleasure that was!

GOD
You'd look ridiculous if you chirped or tweeted.

PENGUIN
I sound like a donkey.

GOD
I wouldn't say that.

PENGUIN
What would you say?

GOD
I would say you are being a little bit of a jackass.

PENGUIN
Would You?

GOD
I might.

PENGUIN
I wonder if You'd say that if You had a flock of this—HONK HONK—in a tree outside Your kitchen window.

GOD
Like you could get up in a tree with those feet.

PENGUIN
Oh, now that's low.

GOD
You're low.

PENGUIN
And You're an asshole!

GOD
The lowest. Thank you for just proving my point. I should have put you in hillbilly attire.

PENGUIN
You've done quite enough THANK…

God snaps his fingers, a puff of smoke explodes in front of the bird. As the smoke dissipates …

PENGUIN
(little scream)

...a mirror appears before the penguin.

PENGUIN
...you.

Penguin is startled at first. Shocked, almost. He truly had no idea he looked so dapper.

PENGUIN
(still impressed)
Wow.

GOD
(at last smiling again)
Yeah. Yeah?

PENGUIN
Look at me!

GOD
Now do you feel bad?

PENGUIN
I look amazing.

GOD
I thought so.

PENGUIN
I mean it. What is this? Feathers? Scales?

GOD
Don't quibble.

PENGUIN
My dry cleaning bill is gonna be horrific.

GOD
It's wash and dry.

PENGUIN
Shut up!

GOD
You shut up.

PENGUIN
I'm shuttin' up!

Penguin goes back to admiring his tux in the mirror. God watches, pleased.

PENGUIN
Boy howdy, are the ladies going to be all over me with this!

GOD
Oh. About that.

Penguin looks at God.

PENGUIN
What about that?

GOD
You only mate once a year.

PENGUIN
I hate You.

FADE OUT

THE CORNER

The Believer

Always be prepared to give an answer to everyone who asks you to give the reason for the hope that you have. But do this with gentleness and respect.

—1 Peter 3:15

NOT THAT ANYONE'S ASKING, BUT JUST IN CASE, I DO SO WITH THE utmost gentleness and respect—this is the best way I can describe my faith:

All my life, I pictured God as this gigantic old man who was just waiting around the corner, His arm pulled high, a big ruler in His hand, ready to smack me with it. But the day I rounded that corner, what I found there wasn't some ogre ready to pummel me with His Stick of Judgment. Instead I felt this presence that did something totally different, totally surprising.

"*There* you are!" this unheard voice seemed to say, with something that felt like enthusiasm. "Finally! I've been waiting so long for you to come this way."

JUST A GIGOLO

The Friend

BEFORE I MAKE A NAME FOR MYSELF IN ANIME, I AM A COPYWRITER at an ad agency. It is my second agency. I was spirited away from my first by one of the city's most brilliant creative directors, Carol Miller. In addition, she kidnapped my fellow writer, Patty Niegos, and it was just the creative infusion her agency needed. Our tenure here began a near decade-long streak of winning awards and multi-million-dollar clients. We are the golden children of advertising right now. Other agencies in town are either jealous of us or they want to hire us for themselves. This is in the go-go 90s and it is a great time to be in the soap-selling business.

I don't know how well you know ad agencies, but to the people who sell you said soap, October 31 is a big deal. It's a holiday tailor-made for all these creative types to show off. Art directors have the distinct advantage over the writers. They possess the hand skills to make any contraption-based costume or wardrobe creation they dream up while the writers haunt the ready-made costume shops hoping for a lightning strike of inspiration . . . or something they won't have to assemble. But the dark horses are all the other people in the agency—accountants, media buyers, and account executives. All year long they're surrounded by semi-artists and wannabe novelists, and this is the one day they get to let their own creative-freak-flag fly. Believe me, Bob the art director will have some serious competition from Marlene in Accounting. Both have been planning for this event for weeks.

I, on the other hand, am a lousy Halloween planner and often find myself on the morning of the 31st scrambling to come up with a costume. I can't tell you the number of times I've gone to a Halloween party dressed as The Guy Who Just Woke Up, clad in pj's, carrying a blankie and a stuffed bear.

Either that or I can't think of anything cool enough on my own so I avoid the issue altogether, feeling like a party pooper all day long as I go through the 9-to-5 dressed like a writer amid witches and demons and slutty cats, which means I'm basically going as a wet blanket. Now, once again, Halloween has come to the agency and I am in a dead panic on the day. I rummage through my closet and the only thing I can find that could even vaguely be misconstrued as a costume is my tuxedo. I briefly contemplate going as a penguin, but looking in the mirror, I realize that I would be the most emaciated penguin the arctic has ever seen. At other times, my gimmick-free closet is a plus, but on this occasion it's a detriment.

Then a light bulb goes off. I grab the tuxedo out of the closet and pick up a pen and paper. I decide I will be a high-class escort, a hooker, a gigolo dressed for an elegant date night on the town. I'll have a menu of deeds and prices posted outside my office door and perform "services" for people all day. In lieu of sex, I'll be offering high-priced slavery. I begin to scribble on a notepad.

Get Coffee	$1
Get Coke	$1
Get Cocaine	$250
Make Copies	$3
Get Your Lunch	$5
Make Your Lunch	$25
Be Your Lunch	$450
Attend Meeting For You	$10
Run Your Meeting For You	$25
Be Your Secretary	$20 per hour

This is perfect. I come up with about five other go-to's and go-for's and, just for shits and giggles, I put a kiss for fifty bucks and a striptease for a hundred. I look at the list, very satisfied with my clever last-minute idea. I'll type up and design an elegant menu on my computer at work and post it outside my office before everybody gets there. Word will spread and, who knows, maybe I'll even make a few bucks outta the deal.

I shower, shave, dress and, after polishing my tux shoes, spray on cologne and walk out the door.

* * *

By mid-morning I am busier than a sex worker in Vegas during convention week. Either people have been dying to make me their gofer, or they are just really, really lazy, but I am making bank. It gets a little slow around 10:30 but all I have to do is hang out on the hall corner near my office and whisper a sly "Hey! Hey, c'mere!" and business is once again booming. Not that I care, but I am a shoo-in to win best costume and get that precious lunch at Chili's or a perk donated by some client. The only one who can hold a candle to my idea is Jo from Production. She wears a lampshade on her head and around her neck is a circular platform that her head sticks out of. Her neck/table is covered in a bedroom-y silk cloth and on top are one condom, one condom wrapper, an ashtray and a pack of cigarettes, and two plastic glasses, one knocked over on its side.

"What are you?" I ask her.

"Guess."

I can't figure it out.

"I'm a One Night Stand," she says proudly.

"We could hot glue a fifty on there and work as a team," I note.

"I'll take my chances, thanks."

By 11:30 I have fetched coffee for ten people, made copies for busy secretaries, and have ordered three lunches. I even peck a couple of girls on the cheek—after they beat me down on the price. I've made about thirty bucks already and it isn't even noon. This is the best costume ever! Not only did it cost me absolutely nothing, it is *making* me money.

All this good-natured Halloween fun comes to a screeching halt when I notice four women huddled together in the middle of the hall by Accounts. They all have money in their hands and as they see me, they stop their conversation and look as guilty as a group of kids standing by an empty cookie jar.

"What are you doing?"

"Nothing." They all say. In unison.

I turn around and walk down the hall and as soon as my back is turned, they start laughing. Then, one of them whistles.

"Hey," June from PR calls out. "What kind of underwear are you wearing?"

I turn back around, cup of coffee in my hand on my way to deliver it to one of the art directors.

I keep walking.

"We're going to find out," April says. Then they all start cackling like pre-slaughtered KFC entrees. Suddenly, the blood rushes to my face. I turn around to see them waving their money.

Oh fuck. It never occurred to me some of these bastards would pool their money. My face feels hot. I begin shaking so much I spill the coffee in my hand.

"God, if I paid an extra dollar, could I get it hot?" the art director smirks when I deliver his cup. "You took forever."

"The girls are pooling their money. They want me to dance at the Halloween party!" I'm already starting to hyperventilate.

"That's hilarious."

"This isn't funny!"

"Oh, yes it is. This is gonna be great. How much is it again?"

"A hundred bucks."

"I bet I can get Jack and Bart to go in with me. At this rate, we could keep you dancing the whole night."

"You can go fuck yourself."

He looks at me with flirty eyes.

"How much if *you* do it?"

I hear him still laughing as I run out of his office.

Back in my own office, I am starting to panic. Surely I can say no. But that would be welching on the gag and make me look like a jerk. It's either look like a jerk or look like an idiot, and I'm not comfortable with either option. I am interrupted by a knock on the door. It's Patty, my fellow writer and a good friend.

"Did you hear?"

"That people are pooling their money? Yes."

"No, that's not what I'm talking about. I just heard that Elena Montemayor's dad died."

"You're kidding." My problems promptly fly out the window. Elena's a friend. Not a close friend, but still. "She's not that old. Was he sick?"

"No, it was sudden. She doesn't know how she's going to get to the funeral. You know she makes all of ten dollars an hour probably."

I can feel the wad of bills stuffed in my pocket and, with it, an idea. If I am going to look like a fool, I'm going to do it for a good cause.

"Holy shit, I could give all my money to Elena. It's not much but it would help a little. I'll put out a memo saying due to high demand, prices have gone up, and maybe people will cough up some serious green."

"Yeah, maybe June Rives will cough up ten K to have sex with you."

"I wouldn't put it past her; she was the first one to pay for a kiss."

"What kind of underwear are you wearing?"

"Tightie whities."

"I'll write the memo. You run to the store."

"Seriously?"

"What song are you going to play?"

"I don't know."

"You haven't thought this through, have you?"

"Not really."

"Wait. Have you even ever *been* to a strip parlor?"

"Uh, no."

"This is gonna be tragic."

* * *

As I speed my car to Gay Town, I am shoving CDs in the player to try and find a song to dance to. Then I find one that would be perfect. "You Suck" by Consolidated featuring the Yeastie Girls. (Yes, that's a real song. Yes, that's who sings it.) The tune has this thumping bass line with a rhythmic jangling, throbbing tribal sound, grinding guitars, and constant, driving beat. The whole song is, basically, a bitch-out to men for not being very adept at oral pleasure for the ladies. The words are just one long screed about how "you suck" because…well, you don't. A sample:

I know you're really proud, cause you think you're well-hung
But I think it's time you learn how to use your tongue
You say you want things to be even and you want things to be fair,
But you're afraid to get your teeth caught in my pubic hair.

And…the indictment gets worse from there. I rationalize the decision to go with this song with the thought that nobody listens to the lyrics anyway.

I know I'm missing prime prostitute time at the office, so I push every yellow light until I get to Basic Brothers.

Basic Brothers is a clothes shop for guys. If there is sexy underwear to be had, this is going to be the place to find it. The G-strings on the silver mannequins in the window are waaaaay to revealing, so I pray there will be something that would leave much of the presentation to the imagination.

I'm ransacking the underwear section. The heavy metal clanging of the hangers sound uncannily like the bells in "You Suck," so I take this as a cosmic affirmation of my choice.

As I am thigh-deep in thongs in all colors of the rainbow, the front door bell announces another customer coming in. On reflex, I look up. The man is tall, maybe 6'5", and obviously no stranger to the gym. He has a five-day scruff on his cheeks and a trimmed goatee. He's handsome, not a pretty boy, and he wears glasses which give him a bookish, almost nerdy quality that keeps his cover-model looks in check. I stare at him the whole time he walks in. I think I swoon. A little.

If only… my mind wanders. Suddenly I remember what I'm here for and get back to the matter at hand.

Finally, I find a swimsuit that's perfect, cut like boxer briefs so they aren't too revealing. They look nice on me. It isn't underwear, but who's going to know the difference?

I go to check out and I see the tall guy has left and I'm a little bummed I didn't get a closer look at him. The clerk rings up the price of the suit, quickly slapping me back into reality. I briefly wonder if I can write this off my taxes.

When I get back, there are people waiting with money in their hands. My office door has five notes on it with names and tasks they want done, each one taped with cash matching the new price point. If this keeps up, Elena is going to have a nice little start to her plane-fare fund. All afternoon I am running errands, answering phones, spelling people while they take a cigarette break. I am getting coffee, making coffee, serving up items from the vending machines. It's crazy. Before I know it, it's time for the party and the only advertising work I've done all day is the hooker menu.

I put in an appearance at the party and a few people wave their money around. I just smile and let everyone keep drinking. A little before 5:00, people are pretty well sloshed. Knowing I can't put it off any longer, I go back to my office, open up my office cabinet and pour myself a glass of vodka for courage. Then I strip off the tux, put the swimsuit on, and get dressed again. Patty is going to be ready by the boombox that has been placed in the lobby for the party. Everything is set. But I don't have a pole or anything really to dance on, no way to designate my space. I look down at my coffee table. It's one big round block, about two feet high. I stand on it to check its steadiness, find it rock solid, and see all I have to do is turn it over on its side and I can wheel the thing out into the lobby and *bam!* instant stage. Seems like everything is magically falling into place.

The lobby is packed. Every one of our agency's fifty-plus employees—plus a handful of people I don't recognize—are there drinking the spiked punch, most in full costume. The agency is on the first floor of a ten-story office building. The space was once a bank, so the entrance is highly visible, two two-story glass doors and a glass façade. Everyone coming into the building on their way to the elevators has a clear shot looking into our lobby, where I'll be dancing. *Great.*

I roll through the crowd with the coffee table. Patty hits the music and dims the lights. Then, as close as I can get to being on the beat, I flip the coffee table over, back onto its base and step on top of this instant mini-stage.

After a few moments of dancing to the music, the vodka kicks in and I realize I can't be just dancing up there forever. I slowly take off my jacket. Once I'm free from it, I hold it high above my head, make a swooping motion, pick out my target, and throw the jacket to one of the art directors. Whooping catcalls are threatening to drown out the music. I notice there are some freeloaders gathering outside the office, peering in through the glass doors. I should have charged cover.

I unbutton my shirt slowly. I do everything slowly. Because the longer the striptease takes, the less time I'll be dancing up here in a swimsuit. I perform the same move I did with the jacket, only this time, I just throw it into the crowd not seeing who catches it. I am so nervous, everybody's faces are just a blur. So far, I think I'm doing okay for a novice. That is, until the ungraceful taking off of the shoes and socks. Here, energy kind of lulls since I have to sit down. Still, there's a good amount of whistling and catcalling. I dance some more. Now the pants have to come off. I hope I can just drop them and step out of them, and while the left leg gives me a little trouble, I manage to do just that. The crowd is going wild. To my surprise, I don't feel like a total jackass.

But now the strangest thing happens. People begin coming toward me with dollar bills in their hands. The brave and bawdy ones slip them in the waistband of my swimsuit. I really don't have to dance that much because I'm so busy taking all the cash. I do, however, gyrate a little bit since they're giving me money and now

I'm *really* into it. When the song ends, there are still people coming to give me money. Everybody's really nice about congratulating me and telling me that I should have won best costume. A couple of girls even tell me I'm sexy. Everyone in advertising lies, but I take it in the spirit in which it is intended. I meet up with my friends who have collected the various pieces of my tuxedo.

"Love the underwear," Debbie Danna says.

"It's a swimsuit," I admit.

"Why didn't you wear a Speedo?"

"I believe the reason for that is obvious."

"Maybe next year. Coward."

"You can't call me coward after what I just did out there. That took balls."

"Balls we would have seen in a Speedo."

"Gimme my pants."

"You made a shit ton of money. Count it," she insists. "Scott has an announcement to make."

While I'm counting my take, Scott, the president of the agency, takes his place on the landing of the staircase in the middle of the room. He's a nice guy, but no stranger to grandstanding, so it's hardly a surprise he claims the dead center of the cavernous lobby to make his announcement. After a brief apology about my performance (to the relief of HR, no doubt) and thanking everyone for coming in costume, he says that there is a down side to the day's festivities, and he mentions Elena's father's passing. Everyone murmurs their condolences to her and she nods toward everyone's concern.

"And the agency is going to match, dollar for dollar, every cent Steven has made today and join him in helping pay for Elena's airfare," he says to appropriate applause, nodding and thanking everyone like he was running for office. Still, it's a really nice gesture. I start pulling cash from my crotch and scramble to count the money.

"Well, Steven, how much did you make?" the president asks.

I kinda can't believe it.

"Well?" Debbie Danna wants to know.

"Uh, I, uh, I made…almost nine hundred dollars," I whisper.

Debbie doesn't miss a beat and immediately yells out to Scott, "He made a thousand dollars!"

While everyone cheers, a little grimace creeps over Scott's face and it's obvious that he didn't really think my haul was going to be that much. Still, a promise is a promise, and he coughs up a thousand-dollar check for Elena later that day. I hand her a huge wad of crumpled cash.

"I can't believe you did this for me," Elena tells me.

"Anyone would have done the same thing."

"No they wouldn't." She looks at me softly. "Thank you, Steven. You made me smile on a day that there was nothing to smile about."

I give her a kiss on the cheek and a hug and we go our separate ways.

I know I wouldn't have made that much money if it hadn't been for a good cause. Personally, I was happy I didn't embarrass myself to the point of humiliation. Nobody got offended, and nobody told me how badly I sucked at striptease. And it turned out to be a great deposit into the karma bank. The day had another payback for me. I just didn't know it yet.

Remember that guy from the underwear store? I wound up, over the next year, running into him just like that at two other places. After the third, we went on a date. We were together seven years and he's still one of my best friends to this day.

I still have that tuxedo, and when I see it in my closet I look at it fondly.

And if I ever do visit a strip club, I'm going to tip those dancers like a motherfucker.

That shit is hard work.

BEAR WITH ME

The Hero

When I was little, I guess about four or five years old, I had a teddy bear. His name was Timmy. Nowadays the only way "Timmy" doesn't sound so cute/ridiculous is if the word "Chalamet" is behind it. But back then, Timmy was a great name to me. Timmy had a hard rubber face with a small upturned nose that had a little ball at the end of it and a smile straight out of a Disney cartoon. The rest of the bear was covered in short blond fur. Petting him was like stroking the head of a GI. I took that bear everywhere.

One weekend, relatives were over to our small house in the suburbs. We generally liked our mother's side of the family but we weren't as close to my father's side. One of Dad's sisters had two little girls, one a year older than me and the other the same age as my sister. We got along well with these children, but his other sister's kids were less agreeable. For one, they were older, the perfect bullying age. They were also very different from my sister and I. We were raised in a very middle-America suburb and these people lived in a rattier house in a sketchier neighborhood in a town about an hour away. Their yard was dirt; ours was grass, lush and green. They grew up hard, I grew up soft. There wasn't a schoolyard playground near their house like there was ours. Instead, there was a ragged creek and tall, mysterious woods. I didn't really know what to make of them then, but the name that leaps to mind now is...what's a good way to put this? Oh yeah: white trash. It was from one of these children that I first heard the word "nigger." So you see the caliber of people I'm talking about here. And they're...*shudder*... relatives. But this is now and that was then, and at the time they were just kids to be wary of.

I don't remember how it started, but at some point during their visit two of my cousins took my bear and were playing keep-a-way from me in the front yard. Being older than me meant they were taller. So though I jumped up and tried to free him from their grip and get him back, I came back down to earth empty-handed each time. The game stopped, however, when one of them threw Timmy too high and too far toward the house and the bear got stuck on our gravel-topped roof. A few half-hearted attempts were made to retrieve the bear but none of my cousins were tall enough and no one produced a ladder. The adults inside were having cocktails and conversation, and to interrupt this flow and have them get a ladder and retrieve the bear was deemed frivolous, and the decision was made to get the bear the next day.

Eventually, night came and my cousins left and I was off to bath and bed. Lying in bed, thinking about my bear, the sky began to thunder and rumble. I grew more distressed, seeing Timmy in my head, up there lying on the rough gravel, afraid of the coming storm, soon to be drenched and cold. Crying myself to sleep seems a bit much but I do remember picturing him up there as alone and afraid as I was just a few feet below him.

In the morning I woke up and ran outside, still dressed in my pajamas. I guess I was hoping to find him on the ground, that he might have blown off in the storm during the night. Instead, I found my father with a ladder but there was no bear. My suspicious adult-self wonders how it was possible for a wind, even a Texas wind, to blow a stuffed animal off a rooftop and then far away where it couldn't be found. What seems more likely to me is that my father found the bear and got rid of it, thinking I was too old for such toys. But that's not like my father. At least I don't think so. But the fact of the matter is, I never saw the bear again and I didn't receive a replacement for him. From that day forward, every adventure I had, I had it alone.

* * *

thirty years later

Business trip. San Diego. One of the ad agency's clients is a home-builder. We've done some image advertising for them, but for the most part it's all "fabulous amenities" and prices in bold.

The builder is undergoing a huge expansion in the west and I am to travel to California with three account executives to tour the properties and the new homes. I am going to be stuck with these women for days and, happily, I like and get along well with the three women I'm going to be traveling with. Lisa is a bright AE, tall and thin with long brown hair and a laser-sharp strategic mind. She's a champion to Creative. Luisa is attractive, short, Latina, and has a smile that is so dazzling she doesn't have to work that hard to get the client to sign on the dotted line. Helen is an older woman, very game, a little bawdy at times, and smokes like a chimney, which gives us plenty of time to get to know each other, because at this time, I am a disgusting smoker as well. She puts me to shame in that department, though, with her near-constant chain of lit Marlboros and me with my Benson & Hedges Ultra Light 100s, the gayest sounding cigarette you can buy at the Shell station. I worked at a runaway shelter when I was in college and one of the kids there told me that the nickname for my cigarettes was Bitches

& Hoes. You'd have thought that alone would have made me stop smoking. Or at least switched to Kents or something.

The three women and I take a cab from the airport to a Four Seasons that is situated between the mountains and the city. A valley is home to all the homes, and the neighborhoods have names like Splendora Point and Buena Vista. One house looks pretty much like the other and you wouldn't be surprised if Jobeth Williams turned out to be your neighbor. But we're not going to tour the subdivision yet. First, we're checking into our accommodations.

The hotel is comprised of a central building, about ten stories tall with other single-story buildings surrounding it. Each building is connected with a roofed walkway that traverses in and out of the hotel building's various entrances. The sun is high and bright and hot and the air is so dry it could crack your skin. We quickly decide it's too hot to have a drink at the outside bar, so we check into our rooms and then meet in Helen's (so she could smoke) and raid the mini bar. We'll figure out where we are going to go for dinner, as we aren't seeing clients until the morning. The night is our own.

After dropping our bags in our rooms and washing off the plane grime, we all meet up again in Helen's room. Lisa is perusing the tiny bottles in the fridge while Luisa stands in the glass sliding doorway between the hotel and the balcony where Helen and I are smoking.

As we are talking, I look out to the horizon. While looking down, two buildings over, I see something on the roof of one of the walkways. I lean over the balcony and squint my eyes. The glare from the sun shining off the white gravel of the rooftop is pretty intense so I can't see the object very clearly, but I know that I see something. I just can't make out what it is.

"What are you looking at?" Helen asks me.

"I see something over there, lying on the roof. What is that? Is it a..."

"It's a stuffed bear on its back with its arms and legs sticking up," Lisa says. "He's in a white T-shirt."

I turn to her, mouth slack.

"I have freakishly good vision," she says casually.

Now that she says this, I can see that, yes, it is exactly that.

"What's it doing up there?" asks Luisa.

"Maybe they tossed him off a balcony," Lisa muses.

"Maybe it was a suicide," Helen says, dragging on her Marlboro before snuffing it out in a Four Seasons-logo'd ashtray.

I listen to the girls debate the bear's fate. Meanwhile, I can't take my eyes off it. I make quick calculations and then look at my surroundings.

Our balcony is a good twenty feet above our own section of roof-covered walkway. Then there is a stretch where it ends, then a gap that's perfectly hop-able, then another section of roof picks up where the other leaves off without the roofs meeting completely. I begin plotting.

"I think I can get it," I nod. My eyes are wild. I'm convinced this is doable. Nay, necessary.

"What are you talking about? How will you get down there?" Luisa asks.

Lisa's totally on board.

"You could jump down!"

"I'd break my leg. It's too high. I need something to lower myself down there."

"I got it," Lisa says and darts into Helen's bathroom. She comes back out onto the balcony with two large cotton towels. "We can use these!"

"Like a prison break," I say, taking the towels from her and trying to knot them up, just like every escape movie I've ever seen. That isn't going so well, so I just loop one into the other.

"You guys are crazy," Luisa tells us.

"Crazy or not, I'm gettin' my camera," says Helen and she ducks inside the hotel room to get one out of her suitcase. Lisa and I test the strength of the towels.

I climb over the balcony, holding on to my end of the towels.

"You sure I'm not too heavy for you?"

I am almost over the balcony, and even though I seem to be a little higher than I initially thought, I don't care. I'm going to do this.

"No, I got you," she says, bracing her body against the inside wall of the balcony. She grits her teeth and holds tightly to the thick cotton towel.

The space is indeed higher than it looks. We probably should be using more towels. But I'm already hanging here, so I decide to just let go and drop down. Gravel crunches underneath my shoes as I land. Lisa holds up her towel, matador-like, *ta-da!*-like, and Helen snaps her picture. I begin walking toward the bear.

When I come to the gap in the rooftops, it too looks wider, just like the balcony turned out to be higher than it appeared. I take a couple of steps back and then run forward, jumping into the air and over the space between them. After walking a few steps, I'm at the bear. Sure enough, he's a little brown, stuffed teddy. The T-shirt he wears sports the Four Seasons logo on the front. I bend down, pick up the bear, and hold it high in the air for my companions on the balcony to see. Cheers all around. Helen takes pictures and I'm immediately glad I have a record of this because if there wasn't, even I would have a hard time believing this is happening.

I'm not exaggerating when I say I have this HUGE sense of accomplishment. I'm no rugged adventurer. I never played sports in school. I've never rock climbed or spelunked. And I certainly never jumped off a balcony onto the roof of a hotel to retrieve a stranded bear. Not until now. I leap over the gap again and then walk back toward my balcony. I cannot possibly feel more manly. My dick must have grown three inches.

It isn't until I'm at the balcony that I remember how high up I actually am. This fact becomes painfully apparent when Lisa leans over and lowers the towel chain, the end of it stopping a good two feet above my raised arms. I can't reach it even by jumping for it. I begin to doubt Lisa's ability to lift me up, not that she's going to have the opportunity to. As the sun beats down on me, I start to sweat and I can't determine whether it's the heat, or nerves that I'm going to be stuck up here. Am I going to have to ask the Four Seasons maintenance department to come get me off a roof? How humiliating. All my heroism will vanish as I'm carried down like a bald Rapunzel. Then I could never tell this story. And do I want to be able to tell this story? You bet your ass I want to be able to tell this story.

"Oh, great. What are you gonna do now?" I hear Luisa ask.

"Toss me the bear," says Lisa.

"Oh, no. The bear's stayin' with me. He got me into this." I shield my eyes with my free hand and scan the surrounding paths of roof. Nothing.

"I'm gonna go see if I can find anything," I shout up at the girls, hoping that by some miracle there's going to be a stray ladder just laying up here for me to use to get back up to the balcony.

I walk north and find another gap in the adjoining roofs. I leap over this one and continue traveling over other walkways. I hop over another space and turn a corner. That's when I see it: There's an A-frame ladder just lying there beside one of the air-conditioning units. It's like it was left there just for me. I swear, when I first saw it, I thought it was a mirage.

I look heavenward. *Seriously?* Then I realize I should shut up before He somehow takes it back. I mumble a quick "thank You" and bend down to get it.

I lift up my shirt, tuck the bear inside, pick up the ladder, and begin carrying the thing toward Helen's room. When I get to the gaps, I have to lay the ladder over so it reaches from one side to the other and then, when I'm over to the other side, I pull the ladder over with me. But other than that, the whole bit is a cakewalk.

"You gotta be fucking kidding me," I hear Luisa say as she sees me coming.

"I know, right?" I admit, still a little freaked out I'm carrying a ladder.

Lisa's thrilled, Luisa's rolling her eyes. Even jaded Helen looks impressed.

I unfold the ladder and climb to the top, then hoist myself back up and over the balcony. I pull the prize bear out from under my shirt. I'm beaming. Seriously, you'd think I've rescued a small child or something, I'm so proud of myself. Believe me when I say the rest of our trip is not nearly so eventful.

* * *

It's not until years later that I put all this together.

It is one weekend where I have my two kids and they are both very young. Sam is about five and Zoe about three. As I tuck them in for bed, Zoe has her stuffed Nala and Simba from *The Lion King*. She moves their faces closer to each other and the hidden magnets within their noses pull the two stuffed animals together in a cute, furry kiss. I look over and see Sam doesn't have any kind of equivalent. I remember the Four Seasons bear and go rummaging in the closet to find it. When I do, I sit down on the bed with him and I tell them both the story of how I came to rescue the bear. Then I kiss them goodnight, turn out the lights, and shut the door.

It takes me a minute or two, but then I remember.

Holy shit!

Three decades ago, I lost a bear to a gravel-topped roof. Three decades later, I find a lost bear on a gravel-topped roof! It might not have been the same bear. It might have been a different roof. But so what? This is amazing.

Something in me feels redeemed somehow. Like I've reached back, years back into my childhood and grabbed the hand of a falling friend. I've heard of things coming full circle. I just never thought it would be something like this . . . and a quarter century later.

I still have that bear.

The present me is too proud to throw it away. And the five-year-old me doesn't want me to.

Five-year-old me can rest now. After all, he's got me to get his bear back. He's got me to protect him.

COMATOAST

The Ingrate

I HIGHLY RECOMMEND COMAS. ESPECIALLY IF YOU'RE PLANNING A move. Going into a coma before a planned move is pure genius. It's not exactly easy to do, of course, but if you can, your friends won't bitch about having to help you move. They'll be too worried you're never going to wake up and see the great job they've done. Going coma is also a prime way to come out to your parents. Lapse into a coma and then have someone else break the news to them. You know the old joke: "Mom and Dad, I have good news and bad news. The bad news is that I'm gay. The good news is I have AIDS." It's kinda like that.

It is a little bit dramatic and it's hard to time appropriately, but if you can pull it off—if drama looks good on you and you've got great timing—it's a brilliant strategy to have. The downside is you take the risk of not ever waking up from said coma. But on the bright side you get some much needed bedrest. Peace and quiet. Pandemonium could and probably will be raging all around you and you'll still sleep like a baby.

But I'm getting ahead of myself.

* * *

I am recently divorced. I had been married for six years and the marriage, despite the arrival of two children, had spiraled into a terrible relationship. But the marriage was doomed to fail anyway. The straight side of the Kinsey scale that I had been inhabiting had progressively disappeared, taken over by the overwhelming gay side. Truth be told, I would have left my wife for a cactus and it would have been a more pleasant relationship. But it's also true that I was (and am) gay. Gay and miserable.

After a year, I not only still feel incredibly guilty, but I miss my children terribly. Missing my two toddlers is almost as bad as being trapped in a horrible marriage. I have the scheduled Tuesday night dinners and the every-other-weekends, but that isn't enough. My arms ache to hold them when they aren't around me. So instead of lifting two children into my arms, I lift glasses of beer, bottles of wine, liters of vodka. Making matters worse, I'm not sleeping. Nor am I eating. I am putting my body through the wringer. And I don't know it, but my immune system is taking a huge hit because of it.

So I don't think anything about it when I am dining in close proximity to others when I go out one night. The occasion is supposed to be just a night out for sushi with my boss and friend Carol. But an old friend of hers named Ron has come into town and she asks me if I mind if he joins us. I don't, so we make it a threesome instead of a duo. We all get along famously and enjoy each other's company immensely. And we all have reasonably fresh breath, which is good, because we are in such close proximity to each other's faces, we might as well be kissing. Or wearing surgical masks. Which would have been a good idea. Because Ron didn't know it at the time, but he is a carrier of a deadly virus. And I am breathing in his infectious air all evening long. So as we sit there, bathed in the blue light from the restaurant's neon sign in the window beside us, tiny microbes are finding themselves a suitable environment in which to thrive: Me.

The next night, I should have gone out drinking again with other friends from work. But on this rare occasion, I decide to go home to my shitty apartment. It is a terrible space, in a falling down brownstone in a funky part of town. Luckily, I was able to find a better place in a better neighborhood and am going to move into that new apartment this weekend. So there is still a lot of packing to do, hence my decision to stay home.

But that doesn't mean I will stop drinking. In the fridge, I find a six pack of Zima, a "malt beverage" that is popular at the time. Zima has a great bottle and the liquid itself is clear, so it's kinda cool. Just because I am in advertising doesn't mean I am immune to the medium's ploys. I'm a sucker for great packaging and a gimmick. So: Zima. But the stuff tastes terrible. Still, I drink it.

Zima doesn't taste so terrible that it induces nausea, however. So I am a little surprised when, just a few Zimas into the evening, I wind up running for the bathroom and throwing up. I don't get alarmed until that sequence repeats itself three more times, until I am throwing up nothing but bile and dry heaving. My head feels hot and my body cold. I have a pounding headache. All of this combines to clue me into the fact that this may be something different than just a stomach ache. I live close to the medical center in town, but the roads are twisty and turny, and when you get down to the med center, the roads are all confusing one-way-onlys. This is years before Google maps are even an idea in someone's head, so I'll never find the place. This is also before there are an abundance of emergency medical clinics in strip centers. So when I remember there is a hospital right off the highway about fifteen minutes from where I live, that seems like the best choice. I get in my car and start driving.

Halfway there, the need to vomit rears its ugly head again and I have to pull over onto the side of the highway. There isn't much of a shoulder, so when I get out I can feel the rushing air of cars passing by me. I make my way to the front of the car and throw up more bile. Then I get in the car and drive the rest of the way to the hospital.

Either I go in the wrong way or it is the nicest ER waiting room there is, because the place where I check in is a wood-paneled room with comfortable chairs to wait in, art on the walls, and plants everywhere. When I get there, there are only two people in the area, the nurse attending the desk and a security officer. She asks me what is wrong and I tell her. She judges me well enough to wait because she sends me to the nearest chair to fill out forms. After I do so, I hand them to her and wait.

My head is still pounding and I instantly regret not bringing a jacket or a blanket. It's freezing. I lean my head against the wall. By this time, the security guard has moved over to talk to the nurse. And whatever they are talking about is hilarious because the two of them are just laughing hysterically and having a high old time. Meanwhile, I keep wondering, *When is somebody going to come and get me?* I fold myself into the chair and tilt my head on the back of the chair next to me. I watch the two talking and laughing, only now they are sideways, like they are standing on a wall. I remember that angle vividly.

Because that's the last thing I remember.

* * *

Now when I say I don't remember what happens next, it's not because my memory is hazy or details have been lost to time. I don't remember any of this because I wasn't there for it happening. This is all based on stories I was told later by everybody who was involved. And there were a lot of people involved who wanted to tell me stories. So this is what happened while I was out:

Somehow or another, Carol is called, along with my parents. The hospital tells them both that I will be fine. Some time later, Carol calls and, for some reason, is put through to the ER. She hears all this commotion in the background. She asks how I am doing and they tell her they'll let her know. Carol then realizes the noise in the background is me. Screaming.

She pauses for a few moments, trying to figure out what to do. Then she calls my father.

"I know what they told you," she says, "but I just called the hospital and things don't sound fine. I think someone from his family should come down here."

With that, my parents grab their car keys and begin the three-hour drive to Houston from the Texas Hill Country outside San Antonio.

When my parents arrive at the hospital, they are told the news:

1. I am in a coma.
2. The doctors don't know how long I am going to be in a coma.
3. The doctors don't really know how I came to be in a coma.

***

They perform a spinal tap on me and discover I have bacterial meningitis. This is years before meningitis became a thing, where there is always the yearly outbreak at some school or college. At this time, this is rare. They can't determine how a reasonably healthy thirty-two-year-old man could contract bacterial meningitis. So the CDC (Centers for Disease Control) is informed and they get involved. An attending physician believes he knows how I contracted it.

"He probably contracted this due to his lifestyle."

My parents don't understand what he's talking about.

"What do you mean, *his lifestyle*?"

"Your son is homosexual."

This is news to my parents. They are surprised by this revelation, but they really don't have time for any kind of reaction. They are too busy wondering if I am going to be alive to talk about it.

* * *

By this time, my friend Karen has come to the ER, along with Debbie, Jimmy, David, and several other friends from work. They all meet my parents, are brought up to speed on my situation, express their concern. Another doctor has told my parents that the attending physician was wrong. My being gay has nothing to do with the disease, that the only lifestyle that put me in any danger was my lousy diet, lack of rest, and bouts of heavy drinking.

The CDC inform my friends that because meningitis is both highly dangerous and highly contagious, anyone who has been around me within a twelve-hour period will have to be placed on medication to prevent it. This basically means that everyone in my office has to take the medicine.

The medicine turns everyone's pee bright orange.

The University of Texas fans are stoked.

* * *

"I want to see him," Karen says. She, being my closest friend at the time, is allowed in. As she goes into the bay where I'm lying, she can't believe what she sees.

My head is enormous, my face enormous. The swelling has become so severe my hands look like Mickey Mouse's. My color is grisly. Somehow my gown is slightly open and she sees my penis.

It, too, is large. (Meningitis benefits!) She gingerly covers me with my gown and leaves.

Everyone is waiting at the end of the hall for Karen to come out. As soon as she exits the double doors, she falters and falls against the wall. Seeing me in that condition was too much for her. David has to catch her before she faints.

"No way I'm goin' in there," says Debbie.

* * *

My parents stay through the night and through the next day; there is no change. I am still in a coma. They exist on cafeteria food and coffee. They call my sister and tell her my progress, or rather lack of it. She says she'll be coming down to join them.

They locate the chapel in the hospital and go inside. There, my parents take their places in one of the pews.

After a while, a nun comes into the chapel and gently asks them if there is anything she can do. They tell the nun the situation. Then the nun sits there quietly and prays with them. This simple gesture affects them deeply. Their spirits restored, they return to the hospital waiting room with renewed hope.

* * *

The ad agency where I work has found out that people from the office are taking off work in the middle of the day to go to the hospital. The higher-ups stop short of putting out a memo, but they do make themselves understood that they want people to continue to do their jobs.

This goes largely ignored and the visits continue.

Unfortunately, there is no change in my condition. At my sister's urging, my parents check into a hotel so they can get some rest, and she takes their place in the intensive care unit. My grandmother has come down with her and they both begin their long, agonizing wait period. Late in the night, my parents return to the hospital and tell my grandmother and sister to go to the hotel, that they've gotten them a room. My parents then begin another overnight shift. Just waiting.

* * *

Now it is day three.

"Wasn't Steven supposed to be moving into his new apartment this weekend?" my father asks.

"Yes," Karen tells them. "You don't worry about that, we'll take care of everything." So my friends band together and divide up the list. Someone rents the truck while a team of people go to finish packing up my old apartment. They will get others to help with the move the next morning.

The move goes smoothly from the old apartment to the new. The women, in particular, are very insistent on everything being just perfect, even if it is still a wonder if I am ever going to live to even see the apartment. I have a blue sectional, each piece slightly curved and movable. You can arrange the sofa in one long curve or turn it into an S. They decide on the S.

"It would look better over here against the window," Jimmy says.

"No, then your back is to the view. I think it should be angled this way," Tricia counters.

"I don't know, it fits better by the window. See how long it is this way and how short it is going the other way? It'll look better here."

"No," she insists. "I think it should go here."

"I don't know. I think—"

"If Steven wasn't in a coma, I know he'd want the couch right here, goddamnit!" Tricia is practically screaming.

Everyone pauses for a moment. Then everybody laughs. Tricia has no inside track on where I want the couch to go. She just decided to play the coma card. And it works. The couch goes where she prefers it.

***

It is some time during the third day that the news comes to my parents: I am out of the coma.

"He's still very groggy. He's still out of it," the doctors tell my parents. The doctors have asked me basic questions, but they encourage my family and friends to get me talking. They aren't certain if I have come through the coma without any brain damage.

After some relieved crying, my parents tell my friends the news and everyone is elated. They want to know when they can see me and my parents tell them to wait a day, I should have my wits about me a little better by then. To what extent, they don't know.

My friends return to the office and spread the news. Management is very pleased.

My grandmother and my sister go back to San Antonio while my parents remain in Houston to see how I am now that I am out of the coma. But the three days of not knowing if I am going to live or die are over.

***

I've been taken out of intensive care and been placed in a room. In the room are my mother and father, my friend from work, Jimmy, and a few others. Apparently I am remarking on a Pretenders' song, "Night In My Veins." I'd been listening to it a lot lately, before the incident.

"It's all about fucking," I tell the room. "Just plain, hard, good ole fucking. On the hood of a car. It's all about fucking."

"Steven," Jimmy says to me, "I don't think your parents want to hear about a song about..."

Then I pass out again.

And that is how it is. Me going in and out of consciousness. Apparently my brain is scrambled, and one of the results is my juxtaposing two situations into one scenario. Or fusing two facts from my past into my present.

Jimmy, David, and Debbie are in my room talking to me, doing what they were advised to do, ask me questions.

"Do you know who we are?" Jimmy asks.

"Yes," I tell them. "You're Jimmy and David. You're the movers."

To my still-addled mind, they aren't Jimmy and David, friends of mine. They are people who were moving me. And little did I know, they were.

"He doesn't have brain damage!" Debbie exclaims and rushes to my bedside. I have known Debbie longer than Jimmy and David combined, nearly six years. "Hi, Steven! We were all so worried about you!"

I look her in the face.

"Who are you?"

* * *

After a while I come completely out of my stupor, and while some people would debate this fact now, I seem to have come through the entire ordeal with my mental acuities intact. But I am not out of the woods yet. Something has gone terribly wrong.

When the meningitis stormed through my body, it left a body-wide case of severe arthritis. Not like the arthritis where your joints ache in the winter or there's some stiffness in the morning when you wake up. But excruciating pain throughout my entire body. I can't roll over in the bed without screaming. Sitting up is agony. I can't get up to go to the bathroom. I continue to pass out from the pain. And all I can do is wait.

I sit there in bed, sleeping most of the time, the rest of it awake and biting the bullet through the intense pain of the arthritis. But it doesn't feel like arthritis; it feels like every bone in my body is broken and the flesh around it has been beaten to a pulp. The only place it doesn't hurt, paradoxically, is my head and my neck. Everything else is torture. I leave the television on to whatever station a visitor has last turned it to. It hurts that much to use the remote.

I have visitors off and on. My ex-wife brings the children once. But none of the visits are very long or very rewarding. Everything is coated in a wash of pain.

After a week of this, I am at last able to sit up and hobble to the bathroom, though everything still brings an amazing level of hurt. It is like my whole body is a sense point and each impression on it, every little movement, sets off a ripple of red hot misery through my bones and my muscles.

It is late at night and I am watching *Bye Bye Birdie* on the hospital television. I don't want to change the channel. Changing the channel means moving. Moving means pain.

I watch a young Ann-Margaret shimmy and sing and I wonder if I would ever be able to move with freedom again. I start to cry. One of the nurses comes in. He is a young Jamaican man, very empathetic, very caring.

"Are you alright?"

"I'm tired," I tell him, "of hurting all the time."

His face grimaces.

"Listen," he says quietly. "We're doing a Wendy's run. Would you like to have some? Give you something different than this hospital food you've been eating for two weeks. My treat."

Nothing sounds more delicious to me.

"Yes. Please."

"Very good, then."

About an hour later, he is back with a Wendy's bag. I lift my arms up and unfold the wrapper of the hamburger. I take one savory bite.

Then pass out from the pain.

* * *

In all this time, you would think I would contemplate my life after what I've been through. My life was hanging in the balance for three days. There was a seventy-two-hour vigil in the hospital with a rotating crew of family and friends. No one knew if I was going to make it out of that intensive care unit alive. But to me? I'd slept through it all, so it doesn't really feel like anything has happened to me. If it wasn't for the arthritis, it's almost as if the event never happened at all. I feel bad my friends had to move apartments for me and I feel bad that I've caused everyone to worry. But as far as reexamining my life or making any grand emotional or spiritual change, there is nothing. Maybe the pain is so intense, that's all I can think about. Maybe it's just denial something so traumatic has really ever happened.

If I am waiting for any epiphany, it never comes.

If I am hoping for some enlightenment, I will go waiting.

If I want a reason for it all, none appears.

* * *

Two weeks have passed and I am able to move around for a few steps with assistance. The doctors say that, at last, I can go home. But I am told the obvious: I won't be able to live on my own for another few weeks. So it is decided that I will go to my parents' house in the Hill Country and be cared for there until the arthritis further diminishes from my body and I am able to move around more freely and independently.

They take me in a wheelchair down to the waiting car and I fold myself in. It is a relief to leave the hospital. The two-week stay was more than enough for me, but I am nervous about the trip home. My body still aches so badly. Every little movement still hurts. I don't know how rough the way home is going to be.

Houston is famous for massive potholes and it seems that my mother, though trying not to, winds up hitting every one the road has to offer. Each time the car jostles it moves me, and even that little jolt causes my body to experience a bolt of pain.

"Does that hurt?"

"Yeah," I grimace.

"We'll be on the highway soon. The road will be smoother soon," my mother says, her hands tightly guiding the steering wheel through the pockmarked streets.

At last, we are through the city streets and onto the highway. The smooth lanes make for a much easier ride and I drift off to sleep. I don't wake up until we are home.

* * *

I am not an invalid, but I am close. I force myself to walk as much as I can, but for the first few days, going from my bedroom to the dining room for meals is the only traveling I am capable of doing.

The entire two weeks at my parents' house, conversations go about as normal, except for the constant questions about how I am feeling. Nowhere in all of the talking is one mention of my homosexuality. My parents don't acknowledge anything and I know nothing about being outed. I don't know if it was them trying to be polite in some way, or they just didn't want to address it. But the subject never came up. And I stay there the whole time, innocent of their knowledge of me.

Finally, after another two weeks at my parents' house, I am able to get about ten or twenty steps with a cane without needing to rest. I feel I can live on my own now. Besides, I want to get to my new apartment and see it for the first time.

* * *

When I first rented the place, I was happy the apartment was on the second floor—no heavy footsteps above me. But when I arrive this time, I am dreading it. Walking is still difficult. Stairs are even harder. Taking them one slow step at a time is excruciating, but I manage it. I take out the key and open the door.

The apartment is immaculate. There is my serpentine airport sofa snaking through the living room, a couple of side chairs there to keep it company. My coffee table is there and there are even magazines laid out, a nice touch from my friends. I have three stained-glass windows that are hung by chains before two torchieres and realize it is a better placement than I would have come up with. The entertainment center is set up with all the components, with a note saying, "Sorry, didn't have the chance to hook up the VCR." I feel bad they are apologizing for not going beyond the call of duty. My bedroom and bathroom are all appointed and the kitchen is even stocked with food in the pantry and items in the refrigerator. On the dining room table, there are fresh flowers. My mail is stacked neatly on the bar.

My parents stay for a while to visit, but want to get back on the road and get home. So we bid our goodbyes and I thank them for taking care of me.

"And you're sure you're going to be alright on your own?" my mother wants to know.

"I'll be fine. I promise. I'll be slow. But I'll be fine," I tell her.

Then they leave and I am alone.

I look around the apartment, overwhelmed by this concrete example of such generosity, and I imagine all my friends on moving day, lifting boxes, unpacking boxes, setting everything up. And the little touches like the flowers and the magazines. Everything is so nice, everything in its perfect place.

I sit down on the sofa.

Then I start to cry.

* * *

My friends' charity doesn't end with the moving in. People come by and check on me, go pick up my pain medication, bring me things to eat. Every time they do, they stay and visit awhile, telling me about the move and that they actually had fun doing it. I hear about the couch placement controversy, whose idea it was to hang the stained-glass windows, things like that. It is all very humbling. And everybody wants to fill me in on what was happening when I was out.

I want to go back to work, but that is still another two weeks away. That seems to be the threshold for major milestones. I was in the hospital for two weeks. I was at my parents' house for two weeks. It is looking like it will be another two weeks before I can return to work.

But I've long since used up all my vacation time and sick time. And it's not like I can afford to be out of work. So my friends at the office bring me things to work on from home, just little jobs to keep me occupied and keep me on the payroll. Whatever empty hours are left on my timesheet are filled up with an hour here, an hour there from everyone who has extra hours on their jobs they haven't used. It is a scam, to be sure, but it isn't one any one of us felt badly about. There is still a spirit of camaraderie and unified purpose and I, its crippled center.

Finally, though, I can't stand it anymore, and even though I still have to operate with a cane, I go back to the office. And life, slowly, starts getting back to normal.

Strangely, very normal.

* * *

The only thing to do in my apartment, really, is to hook up the VCR. Because I am still stiff from the arthritis, it is hard for me to sit on the floor and connect the cables. So one night, when Karen and Debbie are over for a visit, Debbie announces she will take care of the task herself.

"Alright," she says, her voice having a mix of both anticipation and finality to it. "Give me a tape and let's see if I did this right."

I fish around for a movie to put in the player.

"Never mind," says Debbie. "There's one in here already."

Briefly, I wonder what movie I could have possibly left in there, and before I can come up with one, the television screen flares to life. Instantly, that music that can't possibly be anything but a porn score and accompanying moaning fill the room and we are treated to images of two men having sex.

"Oh! My," Debbie laughs.

"Jesus!" I am mortified. "Turn that off!"

"No," interrupts Karen. "I wanna see it. I've never seen gay porn."

So they watch for a few minutes until I can't stand it anymore and hobble over to the VCR and hit the eject button.

"That was hot," Karen says.

"I don't see how that's physically possible," Debbie admits. "I need a cigarette."

We go outside to sit on the staircase. We all light up. It is a hot summer night, but the surrounding greenery of the pool and the light reflecting the blue waves seem to cool it somehow.

"That guy was huge," Debbie marvels.

"I'll say," says Karen. "But I thought it was hot. Didn't you think it was hot?"

"I'm not a big porn aficionado. Unlike Steven," says Debbie.

"It was one tape," I protest.

"Like all you have is one tape," Debbie rolls her eyes. "I just can't believe that guy took that whole thing. Are all gay porn stars that hung?"

"Most," I admit.

"Steven's hung," Karen pipes up.

This surprises me. One, because I can't remember Karen ever seeing my privates. And two, I'm not tiny, but I'm no porn star either.

"What?" Debbie explodes. "I knew it! I knew you two had sex."

"No, we didn't have sex," I tell her.

"We almost did," Karen grins.

"Yeah. We almost did." I, too, smile at the memory. I decide to test her and see if she remembers it as clearly as I do. "Where, Karen?"

"At that convenience store on the corner across from that school. We were getting gas." She laughs.

"That's right. We were getting gas."

She's right. We went at it on the hood of her Jeep. Just like in the Pretenders' song!

"Sounds like you were almost gettin' something else," Debbie says with a sly smile on her face. "If you didn't have sex, how do you know he's hung?"

"I saw it," Karen says.

"When did you see it?" Debbie wants to know.

"Yeah, when did you see it?" I do, too.

"When you were in the hospital. I walked in and, Hello! There you were, that big ole thing flopped out of your hospital robe or garment or whatever it is. I covered you back up."

"Thanks for that," I say.

"Wait a minute," Debbie begins. "You saw this when he was in or out of the coma?"

"In the coma."

"Oh, that's a bunch of bullshit," Debbie blurts out. "Everything on him was swollen at that time. His head was the size of a watermelon. His hands looked like balloons. I'm sure his dick was just as swollen as the rest of him."

Immediately, I am deflated.

"Yeah, you were gonna let us think that," says Debbie.

"Of course I was." Because I *was*.

* * *

There is one other time of note before things go back to being completely normal. Karen is over once more. This time, she is there with our friend David. Again, we are outside on the stairs, smoking cigarettes.

"Steven, I have pictures from that time you were in the hospital," David offers.

It takes me the flash of a second to remember. It has been several weeks since the incident. I have just gotten rid of my cane and have successfully pushed the entire ordeal out of my mind.

"Get 'em! Get 'em out," Karen says excitedly.

David goes inside my apartment, grabs his bag, and takes out an envelope of pictures. Because these are the days when you did that sort of thing.

I look at the pictures in horror.

There I am, feeble and gaunt. My skin is almost gray and there is barely any light in my eyes. Sticking out of the top of my robe are two thin stick arms, one of them resting on a cane. From below, two spindly legs. I can't believe it's me. I am ghostly. I look like I have just been resuscitated. I look like I shouldn't have been sitting up, but rather lying down in a coffin.

"Can you believe that?" David asks. "You've come so far."

As I look back on it now, I wonder why those pictures didn't make more of an impact on me. They should have filled me with gratitude and joy. That I'd dodged a bullet. But there was nothing like that. Nor did I quit my job and join the Peace Corps, or dedicate the rest of my life to helping humanity. If you had looked at my life pre- and post-coma, you would have seen virtually no change at all. It's not like there was this internal, seismic shift in my personality. But shouldn't there have been? There are people in comas all the time and they don't wake up like I did. Why did I get a reprieve and they didn't? Was I such a fighter that death couldn't beat me? Hardly. If Death came after me, I'd probably drop to my knees and just ask he do it quick. I'd probably put up no resistance at all. There are people dying every day. I couldn't understand why I wasn't one of them.

To ponder it today, the only thing I can come up with is that I felt…guilty. I felt guilty that I was the one who was spared, not this man, or that woman. Me. Why? I'm no more special than the next guy. And in a lotta cases, I'm sure I'm much worse. Nevertheless, I was given a pass. And the grace of that is just too much for me to deal with. I didn't come up with any answer so I just avoided the whole thing by continuing along in my life as if *nothing* had happened. And realizing that almost compounds my guilt now, to this day. Even as I write these words, I just feel hollow inside. Am I glad I'm alive? Of course. But back then—and even now— all I feel is guilty. All the photographs did was serve up emotions I didn't want to, or couldn't, deal with. Or process. Instead all I had was guilt. The guilt that somehow I got away with it. Somehow I cheated the system. I beat death. And that didn't make me feel victorious, it made me feel like a crook. The pictures didn't spark me to think of celebrating, they only showed me how close to death I had actually come. And I know I'll be there again some day. And that time I won't be so lucky.

I hand him back the photographs.

"Never," I say quietly but firmly. "Never show these to me again."

SIRENS: A MYTH UNDERSTANDING

The Feminist

LIKE MOST KIDS, I WAS PRETTY TAKEN WITH GREEK MYTHOLOGY when I was younger. Growing up with one angry, sin-punishing Overlord was a little boring compared to the Greeks. The Greek pantheon had a whole host of petty, jealous, and powerful jerks, each with a divine superpower and their own schtick. Apollo was hot, Athena was smart, Zeus was a horn-dog, and Hera was a bitch because of it—that kinda thing. But Zeus wasn't just running around with any old goddess. No, he had a thing for mere mortals. It was flattering to think a god would take a shine to you and come on down, disguised as a cow or a horse and then once you thought they were cute enough to pet, they would reveal themselves in their true form and want to get busy with you. Who cares if he was an animal an hour before? He's a god now! Just look at those arms. My gym doesn't have lightning bolts, does yours?

The Christian God didn't feel the need to disguise Himself when He came down and even then it was only once. The whole thing didn't exactly reek of passion either. In fact, the event was such a non-event an angel had to come down and clarify things for Mary.

"Hey, Mare, listen," sayeth the angel. "I know you're a virgin, so don't freak or anything, but…well…you're pregnant with God's son. There, I said it. Merry Christmas."

When a Greek god fathered a child, the boy was a hero. When God had His…well, we all know what happened to that kid.

Before I became a Christian (and I am a Christian, all evidence to the contrary), Christianity to me was boring and inscrutable, the opera of religions. Greek mythology was an opera, too, but one with soap. Greek gods were catty to each other, they were vain. You know, things we flesh-and-blood folk could relate to. More important than that, they were hot. The male Greek gods were always on the prowl, sneaking around to get a little action on the side. The female deities were (justifiably) jealous goddesses who were prone to punish both the mortal and their mate when the hanky-panky was discovered. When they weren't turning their hubby's intended into a tree or a rock, they were bestowing some cool new superpower on a human dude they thought was just adorable. Greek gods had crushes on their followers. God god was wiping out all his with a flood and giving people to-don't lists all the time. When you worshipped a Greek god, you turned into a valiant warrior with great hair and six-pack abs. You worship God god, your hair looks like you never left the 80s, your politics suck, and people stop inviting you to parties. Greek? You're unbearably hot. Christian? You're just unbearable.

You may not believe all the stories, but they all have a great takeaway. Don't fall in love with your own reflection. Watch out for your Achilles heel. Being Sisyphus is a monotonous drag. Still, there was one Greek myth that always bothered me and I couldn't figure out why. And that was the myth of the sirens. It took me years, but finally I figured out what was wrong with the traditional telling of the tale.

You know the story. Ships of warriors would be sailing back across the Aegean, exhausted from battle, their spirits perked up only by a quick peek into the cargo hold and the loot they were sailing home with. They couldn't wait to get back to their loving, definitely faithful wives and get that hero's welcome they felt they so richly deserved. Because nothing prepares a man for love like war. It's an aphrodisiac with a body count. But then halfway through their journey home, things go south.

Now I don't remember what was first, the song or the singers, but on their way back, these really hot babes on a beach start singing to them. The sailors hear it, and suddenly they can't help themselves. They gotta have these girls. So they steer the ship toward the island.

But they never make it to the island because the place is surrounded by rocks that act like blades in a blender. Jagged jetties tear their ships to bits, which apparently was just what the chicks on the beach wanted. Because they wanted to get their hands on all that loot in the cargo hold. So, men die, girls get rich. For the ladies, it's a win-win.

Now you don't have to read between the lines too much here to see it's more than a little sexist. The men are heroes and victims at the same time. They're like Republicans. The women are just monsters. The men are powerless against their irresistible womanly wiles and are driven mad with desire to the extent they'll wreck their own ship to get to them. But to me this story has more holes in it than the hull of their ship did.

First of all, I've been to the beach and the chances of a nearby Carnival cruise ship hearing me doing some beach-bound karaoke are about nil. So I find it a little hard to believe that these women's song was seducing anybody. And what's with all this beckoning the men to come to shore? You could look at it that way, but what does that say about your worldview? It's much more probable that the men were so filled with their own egos—just sure the women were wanting to fuck them, natch—that they mistook those hand signals. The sirens weren't waving them to come on over, they were warning the dumbasses to get back, there's a bunch of rocks that are gonna bust your ass, stay away. That "song" they heard? More like women screaming a warning, that's what I think. But history has painted these women as manipulative, sneaky, plotting, scheming prick teases who were in it for the money when what they actually were was a group of girls trying to (again) stop a man from doing something stupid.

If this is the true way the shit—and the ship—went down, it'd be just like a man to flip the story so he couldn't be blamed. One variation of the myth even has Odysseus forcing his fellow shipmates to hogtie him to the mast, such was the power of these women's wailings. It's so Camille. *I'm helpless! You've got to stop me!* Because it is, of course, always the woman's fault a man can't keep his dick in his pants.

So the next time you think you know what a woman is saying, you might want to double check yourself and make sure you're actually listening to her. You might be misinterpreting things. Either that or you can't hear what she's saying because you're too busy mansplaining.

Believe me, if men listened to women a bit more, there'd be a lot less shipwrecks to clean up.

So keep on singing, sisters. Don't give up on us yet. Some of us really do care what you have to say.

BOO!

THE ABSOLUTELY TRUE STORY BEHIND GHOST STORIES

The Hyphenate

"I've got your next show," the company attorney informs me.

He catches me when I've just come out of my studio at ADV Films, a company that produces English-language versions of Japanese anime, where I am a writer-director-producer. I'm a hyphenate!

I'm leaving my dark tomb of a studio to get a cup of coffee, go to the bathroom, or smoke a cigarette. Anything to get away from the board and the booth for a moment. Clear my head. The anime I'm currently working on is the midnight-dark horror thriller, *Gilgamesh*. And I've done something different with this show. I've decorated the entire studio to set the mood for the recording sessions and help the actors get into character. Studios are rarely treated like sets. Maybe there's a string of Christmas lights. Stevie

Nicks'll hang scarves. But that's it. Our studio, however, is filled with black skeletal trees, their bases covered in black satin, yards of it, snaking along the studio floor. There's a gilded frame suspended in air, a pour of black silk flowing from it, like water, pooling into a stone birdbath below. Aside from the glow of my computer, the only illumination are candles suspended from the ceiling. My engineer, Adam, and I wear black to the studio every day, just as we've asked the actors to do when they come in for their sessions. It's all great, dark fun, but after working on such a gloomy, moody show, you just need to get away from it for a little bit. See some sunshine.

Now what the lawyer tells me—that he has my next show—is strange for a couple of reasons, but mainly it's because the person who's usually doling out my next show is either a red-haired harridan named Janice or a kindly bear of a man named Joey. Janice always delivers her news through gritted gray teeth, as if she can't stand it that I'm working on any show, much less the one she's been told to give me. Joey's MO is to pop his head in the studio and tell me what my next show is, quickly giving me its closer-than-it-should-be deadline just as he's closing the door. I get some "A" titles every now and then, but a good amount of the time they assign me the shows that have problems. So with the company litigator handing out the show, I can't imagine what's wrong with this dog.

"Why do you have my next show?" I do not hide my suspicion.

"Because I was there when we licensed the title. The show bombed in Japan and the studio just wants to try to recoup some of their money they sank into it. Didn't even charge us a licensing fee for it. Just gave it to us and told us we could do whatever we wanted to it. So John said, 'Let's give it to Steven.'"

John is the owner of the company. A Red-Bull-addicted hurricane also known as Captain Chaos.

I can't believe what I'm hearing. This mysterious show seems to be getting worse by the second. But to do whatever I want with it? That's a little hard to believe.

"You do realize what you're saying," I ask, leery. "This is me you're talking about." I am famous—some say infamous—for my liberal approach with the script. Most of the fans dig what I do with the shows, but there is a small and very vocal contingent that think what I do is something close to sacrilege. So if I have my way with a show, who knows what kind of ruckus I'll stir up?

"Yeah. We know."

Then he starts walking down the hall. My mind is reeling with possibilities. He stops before he turns the corner.

"Oh, you do have to keep the names of the ghosts and the main characters. Otherwise, you can do whatever you want to do to try and get somebody to buy the thing."

"Hey, what is the show anyway?"

"*Ghost Stories.*"

Original line: `Keicherou. Momoko. There you are.`

Fosterized line: `God, can't you just bomb an abortion clinic or something?`

There are dozens of reasons still, after decades of being in the states, anime is not really A Big Mainstream Thing. It's too Japanese. It's too weird. The plots are too labyrinthine. The plots are too stupid. It looks cheap. There's too much violence. There's too much sex. I don't get the humor. My kid gets seizures. It's almost as if anime should come with a pharmaceutical warning label on it. And for some reason, every anime that tries to be spun off into a movie just bombs. Every decade or so there's something that breaks out, like your *Pokemon* or your *Dragon Ball* or a Hiyako Miyazaki film. Or something that tries to, like the manga-based *Alita Battle Angel.* But it's a rarity. None of these arguments against the genre have stopped legions of American fans from continually watching anime series and movies, buying the memorabilia, and filling convention halls with up to 50,000 devotees—and that's at just *one* of the twenty-plus conventions that are held every year.

There are three groups who watch anime. The first and largest group is made up of casual viewers. This group doesn't know and doesn't really care if the original show has been adapted or changed in any way. They just want it to be entertaining. The second group consists of die-hard anime fans who are really into the art form. They may even know of the show before it's come across the globe to America. They may know if a show has been altered in any way, but as long as they enjoy it, they're generally okay with the changes. Then there's the third group, the *otakus*. This Japanese term meaning "people with obsessive interests" has crossed over into English as a specific term for die-hard anime fans—the sort who go ballistic over even the most minute change. And they're very vocal—to the dubbing companies, in online forums on anime sites, on Reddit, wherever—about what they do not like. They're a small but loud contingent. I suppose there is a fourth group, the small number who believe all dubs are evil and that the only real anime is the original, authentic creation in Japanese. But even the otakus will tune them out as too histrionic.

Basically, the trek to American shores goes like this: the anime is produced in Japan, either off a source material like a manga (a comic) or an original I.P. dreamt up specifically for the purposes of broadcast. That content then airs or winds its way through the home video market. Some shows, usually due to their level of popularity enjoyed in Japan, are then licensed to American studios for subtitling and dubbing into English. After these shows are acquired by one of the handful of companies specializing in the process, they are translated, then turned over to production, where voice actors are cast, the script is written to match the mouth movements of the characters on screen, the show's recorded, and finally distributed on DVD and/or to any number of television networks, cable channels, streaming sites like crunchyroll.com or Netflix, or, in rare cases, theaters. ADV Films is one of only a handful of companies that produce dubbed anime. Before the cultural tsunami that was *Pokemon*, a few companies eked out an existence by producing and distributing English-dubbed anime. After *Pokemon*, these companies swelled in size and earnings.

Anime isn't like American cartoons. In Japan, it's a considerable amount of their broadcast content. Some estimates range as high as thirteen percent. Anime accounts for the majority of the country's entire DVD sales. And whereas "adult" cartoons are in the minority in America, in Japan anime comes in all varieties. There's G-rated kiddie fare, more adult PG-13 offerings, and many that would be rated R for their violence, sexual content, or language if they did go to the ratings board. There's even some X, called *hentai*.

The anime market in America alone is more than three billion dollars.

Original line: `Come on, Keicherou! Run! You can do it! I know you can! Just keep running! You'll be ready for the school relay race in no time!`

Fosterized line: `You wanna be an air force ranger`
`You wanna live a life of danger.`
`You don't wanna get raped by strangers`

My journey into anime started with a phone call.

"Hey, Steven! It's Lisa," comes the voice.

Lisa was the production manager at the production house where I edited my television spots for my advertising clients. She left the company a short while ago and I haven't spoken to her in several months. Lisa wasn't just a vendor, she's a friend. So it's good to hear from her, for whatever reason she's calling. And it becomes clear after a few moments that there is a reason.

"Steven, tell me what's happening with the scripts you've written."

"There's only been one that I've sent out to L.A. And that one had pretty good buzz. It didn't get me an agent or anything, but it did get me noticed and I've got several agencies wanting to see what I'll do next."

"You think you're going to be moving out there?"

"I can't. Or I won't, rather," I correct myself. "I'm not leaving the kids. Not until they're eighteen at least."

"Good."

"Well, it's good and it's bad."

"What about your Addy sweep?"

I had recently cleaned up at the annual advertising awards show, besting agencies ten times my size. I am on a career high. But truth be told, I am getting a little tired of advertising. I feel like I've done all I can in that business. I've worked for other agencies and won awards, made lots of money. I opened my own little shop and did the same.

"What about it?"

"How happy are you with advertising?"

"Okay, okay, what are you after?"

Now she knows she has me.

"When I left POV, I took a job at another company in town. ADV Films. They produce English-language versions of Japanese anime. Do you know anime?"

"No," I admit.

"That's okay. I didn't either. Listen, I think there's a position here that you'd be perfect for. We're looking for a writer and a director in one. And when you're recording your radio spots, you're basically directing, yes?"

"Yeah, you could say that."

"How about you and I have lunch? I can tell you more about the job and the company, and if you like what you hear, we can zip over to the studio, I'll give you a tour. Maybe you can meet the owner and president, and we'll go from there."

So we make plans for lunch. After I hang up the phone, I replay what she said. A film company that's doing cartoons? In Houston? Seems like a reach.

Over lunch Lisa elaborates about the company. They are small, maybe twenty employees, and most aren't really professionals but anime fans or friends of the president and his co-founder. They started out as a small gaming company when the future co-founder told the future president about the underground anime market and how there is such a devoted cult following that they will pay for shitty bootleg VHS tapes of anime shows from Japan. He floated the balloon about doing a more professional version of that and seeing how it sold. Because of the video game company, the guy had connections in Japan and he used those to get into contact with various Japanese animation studios. So they staffed a tiny office with friends and fans and produced one subtitled video. It sold more than they anticipated, so they decided to produce another. That one did even better, so they flew to Japan again and licensed a couple more. This time, they would produce an English-language version of the show, so they built a small studio in a dumpy section of town and opened up this small production company. That title did exceptionally well and now they are up to their necks in licensed product and they have to hire someone to come in and assist in the writing and directing duties. All the dubbing is being handled by one of the co-founders and he can't humanly produce them all, so it's time to look outside the company. Lisa has been hired to streamline production processes, give the place a professional makeover, staff it accordingly, and ramp up production. When she saw there was a need for a writer-director-producer, she thought of me.

I agree to a tour of the facility. Now that she has me on the line, she begins to leak more information about the company. She tells me not to expect much. She says the employees can be a little… different.

When we arrive at the studio, I see that it's definitely not there to impress. The space is a bland, beige strip center in a lousy part of town. Their neighbors are knock-off cologne stores, T-shirt printers, a handful of sketchy restaurants, and cell-phone accessory stores that are probably money laundering operations. Lisa uses a key card to gain access into the clouded glass door and we step inside. There, more beige—a warren of offices. The waiting area, such as it is, consists of a beat-up maroon faux-leather couch and a dying ficus. Instead of framed art on the walls, there are sad cloth scrolls of anime characters. The company copier sits right beside the lobby. There is no receptionist. The place is a bonafide dump.

Lisa gives me a tour of their tiny offices. There's a small art department filled with artists hunched over their glowing computers designing box art and sales materials. There's a couple who've been with the company from the beginning who are or aren't married—it's hard to tell by their interactions—but they're very strange. There's a skeevy sales guy. And a real slick sales guy. There's a small accounting department and a small warehouse of product with one man manning the shipping. There's the co-founder of the company, a man who's a dead ringer for Peter Jackson (the heavy version) and whose passion for anime is, shall we say, longwinded. And at last, there's the amped-up president and other co-founder of the company, an ADD head case with beady eyes and large, round, pale face that looks like he's eternally surprised. (This is the man I will later christen Captain Chaos because of the maelstrom he can create in every department in the company.) He pumps my hand quickly.

"Hi, Steven! Nice to meet you! Nice to meet you! Lisa tells me a lot about you! Lotta good stuff about you!"

"And I've heard a lot about you. This is quite a place you have here." No, that's not a lie.

"Is she giving you a tour of the place? Whadya think? Pretty cool, huh?"

"Oh, yes, sir, it's very cool. Can't wait to see the studio." Okay, that's a lie.

"You're gonna love it! We're expanding very fast here and we're looking for someone like you who can come in and hit the ground running. Lisa tells me you're that kind of person!"

"I'm a quick study. So far I haven't seen anything to scare me off."

"Good, good! I'm sure we'll talk soon! It was good meeting you!"

Then he's off, chugging a Red Bull as he goes.

Lisa says she'll take me to the studio. To my surprise, we have to go out the door we came in from, to the outside of the building. We then walk about fifty paces, past more clouded glass doors, to another passkey-locked door at the end of the building. We then re-enter the same building, albeit a different office. Inside is a studio that looks like it's been put together with less of a budget than a community-college radio station. There is a small room for processing equipment and then a larger room with a sound board, a monitor in front of it, two large speakers, and two desk chairs. There is a glass sliding door and, through this, is another room with a small recording booth built into the corner. In that booth is a mic, copy stand, and another monitor. The sliding glass door isn't like some special office divider. It's like the sliding door from the back of a house. It looks weirdly out of place and seems to serve no real purpose since the booth is already soundproofed. At least it looks soundproof.

"We're not recording right now. I think Matt's writing his next show," Lisa tells me. "Here's where the engineer and the director sit as they're recording. The talent is in the booth there."

I stand behind the director's chair. You can't see the booth from here.

"He can't see the talent?"

"Well, you have to stand up and lean over like this if you want eye contact with them," she explains quickly.

"Aha."

"Okay, I know it doesn't look like much, but we're growing. We're expanding. In a year or two, this place will look totally different. At least that's..." She looks around the room and then motions her head toward the front door and we walk outside once again. "I know how it looks. But really, they're changing. They want to grow. They want to get better. They have to. I've already helped them streamline their art department and the production processes. I'm working on getting another engineer in here because we only have a part time one now. I know it doesn't look like much, but trust me."

"I believe you."

"You do?"

"Yeah," I chuckle a little. It's funny to see her so...well, kind of embarrassed about the place. She's got no illusions, which is reassuring. "I do."

"Good. I know what I thought when I first came here. But it's changing. I promise." She starts walking me back toward the other door. "How about this?" she asks as we walk and talk. "Why don't I give you a VHS of one of our shows? And I'll give you a VHS of a show we're going to record. You write an ADR script for it."

"What's an ADR script?"

"Automatic Dialog Replacement. You take the translation and then turn it into script that looks like it's coming out of the character's mouth. If you've done it right, the viewer won't even know it was originally in Japanese."

"Got it."

"That way you can see if you like it. You may love it. And if you do, we can talk about bringing you on. How's that sound?"

It sounds like a plan to me, so she gives me my packet of materials and I'm on my way.

Once I'm home, I watch the movie she's given me. It's an action piece, no great shakes. The acting is terrible. Really hammy. If my job is to do it like this, I'll have to pass. If they want the acting to be better than this, yeah, I can do that. I put in the tape of the show I'm to write a script for and press play.

I dart my eyes back and forth, from the printed translation in my hands to the screen in front of me. I say a line where the character says it. Then I hit rewind and say it again. It doesn't look right. I scribble another version of the line and try that one. That seems to work. I do this repeatedly for hours. It's tiresome, frustrating, tedious work. But the more I do it, the more I get the hang of it and it starts to take me less time. And, after a while, I find a rhythm and realize I have kind of a knack for it. When I'm finished with my script, I watch the entire twenty-two-minute show and read my script along with the video to ensure it looks as perfect as it possibly can. I go to bed late, but proud of myself.

A week after I turn my script in, I get a call from Lisa. She tells me Matt, the co-founder of the company and only other director they have, says my script is pretty good and he thinks it will work. He'll know better when he goes into the studio to record it. She also tells me John, the president, has already signed off on me. I tell her that I hated ADR scriptwriting at first, but once I got the hang of it, I really enjoyed it. I ask her about the acting and she says what I heard was just Matt's "style" and that I could direct the talent however I thought best, which is a huge selling point. But what really sells me on the company are the people. Animated characters may have been on all the monitors and TV screens, but the real characters were the actual people working there. They're a ragtag, motley group of dorks and dreamers. And I really liked the combination of nerd/fanboy expertise of Matt complemented by the rush-rush all-business of John. I tell her that I'll come in to meet with the president of the company to talk salary, and after I do that, if all goes well, I'll be starting in a couple of weeks.

The meeting with the president goes well. Captain Chaos has even more energy than I do—that's saying a lot—so he's a lot to handle, but I like him. He agrees to my salary request and says he's in line with my projections of future earnings based on my performance and we shake hands. I'm to start in a month.

Now all I have to do is have a talk with my advertising clients. I'll explain the situation, tell them I'll stay on and finish all the work I've started and any project they'd like to get done before I leave them. I'll have a list of other agencies and freelancers that I've vetted that can capably pick up where I leave off. Then RocketBoy Communications will close its doors for good. I'll leave the ad world, going out on top. Everything falls into place and, more importantly, feels good, exciting, challenging, and new.

I go through my office and pack up all my advertising spots and TV commercials for storage. Before I box up the radio spots, I play the one that stormed at the Addy awards, just for old time's sake. I put the cassette into the player and hit the play button. Immediately a sultry, sexy voice starts purring.

"I hate my real name. So I go by Karyn. With a Y. I have very long hair, light brown, like sand, highlit with blonde lights. It has the consistency of silk. I work at it. And if you look at it just right, it actually sparkles. My skin's a soft, smooth bronze so perfect it says, 'Yeah, I just got back from Belize.' I'm 5'8", 116 pounds, and my measurements are 36, 24, 34. I sing and I dance. And right now I'm wearing a little black silk Donna Karan number with a slit right up to my…well, you can imagine. I'm looking good. You could say I turn heads. And you know what? You'd be right. And I have to admit, when I'm looking this good, and everyone's looking at me, it makes me feel pretty damn hot."

Then a gruff voice like a bored football coach barges in.

"Drag Night at JR's. Come in and be yourself. Or not. JR's. For boys and girls. And boys who like to be girls."

I smile and say goodbye to advertising.

Original line: `I understand you're worried, but you can't see her rightnow.`

Fosterized line: `Are you a very close friend of hers? Oh you poor little precious lamb. She's a goner.`

Formally, I am brought on board ADV as a writer, director, and producer. But very quickly I will also become talent scout, production designer, systems analyst, interior decorator, voiceover talent, accountant, publicity director, salesman, marketing department, dancing monkey, and janitor—in addition to my gig writing and directing the English-language versions of the shows. I am hired with the charge of making the shows more accessible to American audiences. This is fine with me because, while I like the shows, to me the scripts' language can often be a little pat. Maybe this is because it's just a direct translation and there is always *something* lost in the translation. Maybe it's just a matter of taste, but I think the dialogue can use some tweaking so I'm more than happy with these marching orders.

The dubbing process begins, as everything does, with a script. And this script is an exact translation of the anime. That means that someone who speaks both Japanese and English literally sits down in front of a television set or computer screen and watches the show in Japanese, translating every line as they go. This translation is then turned over to a scriptwriter who pens the ADR script.

The original Japanese lines are usually much shorter or longer than the English translation, so there are some liberties you have to take with the line in order to make it physically work within the anime itself. For instance, if you tried to use just the direct translation, you'd come up five or twelve or twenty lip flaps short or long. Lip flaps are what the movements of the anime characters' mouths are called. So you have to elongate (or shorten).

Here's an example:

Translation: `Hi, Billy. Say, I really like your shirt. It's cool.`

ADR Script: `Hi, Billy, what's up? Hey I really like that shirt you have on. It looks cool on you.`

Some fans go ballistic over script changes like that. But most fans accept them. They know the translation isn't going to be perfect or right for the animation when it gets revised into English.

But I tend to push this even further. If it serves the story better, I'll even change the whole meaning of the line. The principle I generally use is that if it's something that doesn't advance the action or is necessary to the plot, I can change it. Now I stick with the *character* of the script. In other words, I don't have a milquetoast character suddenly cussing a blue streak. I just make him more milquetoast, give him something more interesting or funnier to say, or just elaborate on his character. The degree to which I do this generally depends on how rabid the fan base is for a show. If there are thousands of fans dying for a show to come out in English, I don't change very much. If it's a mediocre show, I don't change very much. But if it's troubled, boring, or just not funny, or if it's a show that has some potential to be something great, I can do extensive rewrites on that series or movie.

Below is a line from a show called *Orphen*. In this scene, two trolls are running up to Orphen, ready to beat him up. One troll, Volkin, has a bucket on his head and he's wielding a mop like it's a sword.

Original translation: `Alright, we're going to get him. Ooh, he'll be sorry he messed with us!`

My version: `You kick him in the shins. I'll hit him with the mop. You got that? Stick with the plan!`

See? It's totally changed. Am I still getting the message across? Yes, of course. The new line plays with what's happening on screen more than the original. And to me, it's just funnier. But it's script changes like this that have got me a reputation. Some people love me. Other people loathe me. Luckily the lovers outnumber the loathers. I am so notorious, my "style" has been coined a term that is now in the Urban Dictionary.

foster-ize. v. the act of breaking, butchering, or fucking something up that was perfectly fine for no reason other than personal satisfaction.

Of course I don't agree with the definition exactly. I don't think the original was "perfectly fine" and I don't change it for "personal satisfaction." I change it because I feel it needs changing. But I'm not going to complain. I've never been a verb before! And for the record, no Japanese studio or creator ever complained about any of my script changes. Not once. The only people who get in a tizzy about it are some of the American fans. And my shows sell. They sell well and, usually, over projections. Rest assured that if what I was doing didn't work, someone would be curtailing my liberal treatment of the script in a heartbeat. Like the saying goes, it's show *business*.

I'm really, *really* good at my job. When a special project or another studio comes in, they give that project to me. When Sony wanted to bring their beloved *Appleseed* franchise into ADV, I was the director and writer on the job. When the video game company behind the blockbuster game *Halo* was looking for a studio to dub a series of anime shorts they had produced, they put me in the chair. When Captain Chaos wanted to have a national anime awards show, I was tapped to write and direct it. When he realized the studio was a dump and Sony was coming in for a tour, guess who was tasked with redecorating the entire place? That would be me. I'm one of the fastest directors the company has and one of its most efficient producers. All my shows come in on time and under budget. I was the first director to put extras on the DVDs. I decorated the studio for recording. I've held premieres at the local Alamo Drafthouse to announce a new series. I've conducted photo shoots of the actors in the cast for publicity purposes. But my biggest achievement is the improving of the recording process.

Originally, the way shows were recorded was there was a master script on paper in a large three-ring binder in the booth with the actors. When a line needed revising (and they almost always need revising), the director would have to come up with the new line, tell it to the actor, and then the actor would write that new line in the paper script. It was tedious, it cost money (in time), and made the actor play secretary in addition to doing their normal job of acting.

I thought that surely there was an easier, more efficient way to do this. Maybe a way where the talent in the booth could see what my computer screen looked like. I would have the script up on my screen (which is also their screen) and would just retype the line right away digitally and no one would have to play secretary but me. I get with the tech people and they rig up that system just as I designed it. It is a huge success, saving hassle, headache, time, and money. And since the script isn't down at chest level anymore but up on a monitor, the actors are always on mic instead of sometime going off mic because they're bent down reading a paper script.

This script treatment works out in another big way. By this time I have done this for six years and am really good at writing script on the fly for the lip flaps. Occasionally I'll have a scriptwriter pen an ADR script for me, but I always wind up preferring my own script to theirs. I'm like a chef. No one in the kitchen but me. But with this new recording procedure, it's possible for me to go into the studio with just the translation and come up with the lines as we record them. And because I'm so fast, it doesn't really add significant production time. And I'm saving the money that would usually go to a scriptwriter. It also keeps things spontaneous and fresh because things are imagined right there, on the spot. I don't know if it's the pressure or what it is, but I'm insanely creative in this way. Maybe I'm just really good at revising other people's work. At any rate, this system I designed is still in use to this day and saves the company hundreds of thousands of dollars in production costs every year. I test this new procedure during the recording of *Gilgamesh* and it works perfectly.

This will end up being invaluable for my next show, *Ghost Stories.*

Original line: `I haven't done my homework.`

Fosterized line: `Lunchtime bj? I'm in, dude.`

After the company lawyer dropped the news on me, my engineer comes out of the studio. Adam is a tall, handsome, mixed-race young man with an incredibly personable demeanor and a wicked sense of humor. He's the best engineer I've ever had and I've had all of them—oh yeah, that's another one of my jobs here, break in new engineers.

"What's up?" Adam asks.

"I just talked to Griffin. He told me what our next show is."

"What is it?"

"It's called *Ghost Stories* and we can do whatever we want to it," I say, still slightly shellshocked.

"Bullshit."

"Swear to God."

"Anything?"

"Practically anything."

"Aw, dawg, you're gonna tear that shit up."

But first things first: Adam and I have to wrap up *Gilgamesh*. After we do that, I go to the production manager's office and receive the translations and VHS tapes for *Ghost Stories*. I work from home for a couple of days to see what the show is about and see what I can possibly do with it.

The show is basically a lame *Scooby-Doo* ripoff with a cat where the dog should be. Five plucky youngsters—in this case, elementary school kids—battle a ghost-of-the-week each episode. Each episode is a totally contained show. Only the pilot episode really demands to be watched in a certain position. The others you could shuffle and never be the worse for wear. The show's animation isn't bad, but it's nothing special. The show just paddles along on its mediocre legs, not really harming or healing anyone in the process. It's a *meh* show in all ways possible. And it's my job to turn it into something wonderful. I start with the characters.

The heroine of the group, Satsuki, is a fiery little girl with a spunky spirit. She and her father and her little brother move back to the town where her mother went to elementary school. Turns out her mother was a girl who put restless ghosts to "spiritual sleep" when she was young, and she kept a diary of each ghost she banished to the otherworld as a sort of how-to book. It's a good thing, too, because now nearby construction has disrupted all the ghosts' sleep and they're waking up and wreaking havoc.

Helping her in this task is Hajime, the supposed love interest (though nothing ever really happens between them); Leo, a nerd and "psychical researcher"; Momoko, an older classman; Keicherou, Satsuki's little crybaby brother; and Amanojaku, their cat who, in the first episode, gets possessed by a demon who isn't too keen on helping the kids in their ghost-fighting pursuits.

There's an episode about an artist ghost, a snow ghost, a headless biker ghost, etc. The violence is fairly intense. Some of the scenes are a little rough for younger viewers and the ending song that rolls over the credits is called "Sexy Sexy," so it seems a little mature to be strictly a kids' show. But it's so juvenile it doesn't really feel like it's for an older audience either. Maybe that's why it tanked in Japan?

Who knows. This is a country that has vending machines with used panties in them. Eventually you just stop asking questions.

I watch all the episodes and then try to let my mind go crazy and see what I can do to spice up these characters. And that's where the fun comes in.

Original line: `I like the internet. I use it all the time to research things for my upper division classes.`

Fosterized line: `The internet was a blessing from the Lord Jesus. Until Muslims and pedophiles stole it and used it to seduce little children like yourself into sin.`

After a few days of brainstorming—and a couple of concepting sessions with an icy martini in my hand—I land on a few good ideas. I'll make the lead girl, Satsuki, a rampaging feminist. And she won't take any guff off of Hajime, who I'll make her foil. She'll be well-versed in pop culture—politics, entertainment, the works. In fact, I'll make them all pop-culture savvy, which should give me a wealth of material to work with for gags. Taking a cue off of a panty shot that Hajime gets of Satsuki, I'll use that and run with it and make him a little horn dog.

When news gets out that I'm going crazy with this show, I'll undoubtedly get a lotta heat. I figure I can temper some of that if I cast all anime favorites in the leads. So I pretty much cast, sight unseen, Hilary Haag as Satsuki. Hilary can lighten her voice and make it a little higher so she sounds younger. And no one sounds funnier pitching a fit than Hilary. I cast Chris Patton as Hajime because he can play both smooth and slippery. For Leo, the nerd, I cast Greg Ayres, who can whine wonderfully. All the actors have great comedic range, so I should be able to get some stellar performances out of them, provided I give them good script to play with. To make Greg's character more interesting and give him a little more comic potential, I decide to make Leo Jewish and give him all the stereotypical traits that comes with that. This show will not be PC. Momoko, the elder classman and supposed "looker" of the group, is a crashing bore. I have no idea what to do with her until genius strikes suddenly and I make her a devout born-again Christian. She'll spout scripture and be hugely judgmental of all the others. I'll cast Monica Rial who has the sweetest, most innocent voice you've ever heard. She'll be just right for Momoko. I'll have to audition someone for the part of the crybaby younger brother, Keicherou, as playing someone who's six years old is kinda tricky. It'll probably be a woman who gets the part. Most men who try to sound like little boys sound exactly like that, a man pretending to be a little boy. And all this character does is cry all the time. And he's a little stupid. So I decide to crank that up to eleven and I make the character retarded. I mean, mentally challenged. (But if stuff like that offends you, then you're going to have a really hard time with *Ghost Stories*. I take no prisoners.) I eventually cast Christine Auten in the role because she cries and speaks just like a little boy. For the demon-possessed cat, I cast the comic Rob Mungle, and I'll dial up the snark on the cat tenfold.

Armed with a main cast and characters, I begin to write the first episode just to establish tone. I'll write all the other episodes in the studio as I go. It's a risk, but I think I can do it. It went well with *Gilgamesh*; it should go well with *Ghost Stories*. And instead of writing it alone, I'll be writing it live with my engineer and the actor in the booth, so I'll have an immediate reaction if something is funny or not.

I'm beginning to get very excited.

Original line: `It wasn't the right size. So it was a little loose. Her fiancé said he'd get a new one` made. But she wore it happily on her finger every day. She must have been wearing it on the day of the accident. The police said it must have flown off on impact.

Fosterized line: Her fiancé was engaged once before. Probably to some fat girl. Wynona Judd. Carnie Wilson. Maybe Nell Carter. Where's the justice? Here this loser finally finds this attractive, THIN girl to marry and she has to die! She never did get to do the things she wanted to do. Cure cancer. Win the Nobel Peace prize. Have a four-way.

I talk to all the actors I want for the main cast and throw them in the booth, just to make sure those voices look right coming out of the animated characters' mouths. My instincts are dead-on. The cast is perfect.

The recording process goes amazingly well. I'm coming up with lines as we go, and thankfully, almost all of them get a laugh reaction from Adam and the actors. If it doesn't get a laugh, I just write jokes until we find one that we all find funny. It feels like a collaborative process and I'm playing well to the crowd (of two at a time). Having to write in front of an audience is incredibly thrilling and I take to it like a mallard to Evian.

Happily, all of the cast are having a blast with their roles, and occasionally, a few of the actors pipe up with a joke or two of their own. This gives me an idea: instead of taking sole credit for writing the show, I'll share credit with the main actors of the cast. I figure if it's not just me who's supposedly writing the show, but some of the fans' beloved actors, they might not judge it as harshly. It's a little bit of a lie—well not a lie exactly, more like an exaggeration. But I'm really loving this show and what I'm doing with it; I don't want it to get unfairly judged just because it has my name on it.

It's not just the main characters that I'm having fun with, but even the special guest stars of each episode are being tweaked. Instead of your average, run-of-the-mill, generic characters, I'll goose each of these walk-on parts and make them choice roles for actors, ones they can really sink their teeth into, just as the main characters are. A girl in the pet cemetery episode becomes a bipolar animal lover. A female hairdresser will transform into a mincing queen. A superintendent for an apartment complex will morph into a bitter almost-pedophile. Every stereotype makes an appearance and is exploited, and I'll hammer out the most gasp-inducing, did-they-just-say-that? script I can. As a kids' show, this one is definitely more *South Park* than *Sesame Street*.

Taking the initial charge to heart, I'm keeping the character names and the ghosts, but everything else is up for grabs. Everything else is changed.

Below is an example of just how drastically the script has been altered. And this isn't a conversation with the main characters, this is just a random expository scene with a group of construction workers. The first section is the translation. What follows is my version of the script.

Original translation:

```
                CONSTRUCTION WORKER #1
    What are we supposed to do with these boards?

                CONSTRUCTION WORKER #2
    Just leave them over there. No one's going to
                     complain.

                CONSTRUCTION WORKER #1
```

Okay. (grunt)

(then, looking at map)

So there's an alternate route, huh?

CONSTRUCTION WORKER #2

Thanks to that, we can still block off traffic here and do the bulk of construction.

CONSTRUCTION WORKER #1

(grunts twice)

WORKER #1

Why was that tunnel closed off?

WORKER #2

Well, a long time ago during the construction, a lot of people got killed.

WORKER #1

Come on! I can't handle stories like that!

WORKER #3

Anyway, those were rumors.

DRIVER

It's starting to get foggy.

(looks in rearview mirror)

What's with that guy? He's going really fast.

WORKER #3

Hm? What an old model. It's a Bluebird from the 1970s.

DRIVER

Going that fast…he better be careful he doesn't get into an accident.

Here's the same script, fosterized:

WORKER #1

What am I supposed to do with these boards?

WORKER #2

Just move the boards over there, board mover.

WORKER #1

Sure thing. (under breath) Jackass.

So why'd they close off the tunnel anyway?

WORKER #2

Years ago…people went into that tunnel and they didn't come out. Not unlike your sister.

WORKER #1

Hey let's get off of sisters okay, man? Especially since I just got off of yours.

WORKER #3

(in a Hispanic accent)

He-he-he. I like his sister. She's one hot chulo.

(pause)

DRIVER

I know that you're gay.

(looking in the rearview mirror)

Oh great, you'll like this. Somebody's on my ass.

WORKER #3

Slow down. Slam on your breaks, eh? Workman's comp.

DRIVER

With my luck he's probably your cousin. With no damn insurance.

So…different, yes? But what really sells every joke is the way they're all delivered. The actors make every single line come alive. Their intonations and timing are as good as any Warner Bros. cartoon. I couldn't be more proud of them. Even one-off lines from passersby are given a comedic twist. The first episode leans a bit more closely to the original script, just to set up the premise. But with each episode, the revisions grow more and more extreme, ever more daring. By episode four, almost every single line has been rewritten with a comedic bent. After seven years of going by the book, so to speak, it's liberating doing whatever I want. The *Ghost Stories* script is the most "me" show I've produced. The humor is totally my whacko sensibility and I'm having the time of my life recording it. Some days my engineer and I are in tears we're having so much fun. It's incredibly rewarding seeing something that came into the studio wilting like the dying ficus in the company lobby and then having it blossom into something that is, in its own way, beautiful. Depraved, offensive, gleefully subversive, and foul-mouthed, but beautiful nonetheless.

When we finish with all twenty episodes, they're sent to mix and I begin the letdown of moving on to my next show. I know nothing will compare to the fun I had with *Ghost Stories*. After a couple of weeks, I go in to hear the mixed episodes, and happily, they're just as funny as they were when we recorded them. The mixer himself tells me he's never worked on a funnier show.

A few months later, the DVD is released and the reviews are in. Before I got into this business, if I heard an actor or director say they didn't read their reviews, I thought they were full of shit. But now I totally understand the inclination. I don't want to read the reviews when *Ghost Stories* comes out. But unfortunately, I have to because each show's writer also pens the text on the packaging, and I need to find review lines to quote on the boxes. The first round of reviews are favorable, although most of the reviews dodge the review part and instead debate on whether or not we "should" have done such a hatchet job on the show. As far as the general public goes, people who haven't seen it are, of course, bitching the loudest. Everyone that *has* seen the show agrees with our first analysis of the show. The original is a crashing bore and if we hadn't done something like this, the show would have bombed and faded into obscurity. Now at least it's a conversation piece. But as each volume gets released, the reviews go from kind to crazy rave. I have no trouble at all finding complimentary slugs for the box text.

The one time I check the fan chat rooms, the debate rages but the pro-Foster voices are greater in number than the antis. Somewhere along the line, rumors started that the show was all adlibbed by the entire cast, which is (1) not true and (2) my fault because I was too chickenshit to be listed as the only writer. A few of the actors—ones who are in touch with the fan community, like Greg Ayres and Monica Rial—tell me that all the people they talk to are overwhelmingly positive about it. But I'm terrible about living in the moment, so I really don't just sit back and bask in the glory of a job well done. And that's the suck thing about anime production. In usual TV and film production, a director or writer or actor gets to rest in between projects. With anime, as soon as one is done, another slides right in to take its place in the queue. But I'm happy with the show, the cast is proud of it, and the fans seem to dig it. I count it as a positive experience and move on.

At the end of the year, however, comes a nice surprise. The premier publication for anime, *Anime Insider*, gives *Ghost Stories* the award for Dub of The Year, which is a huge compliment. And that's the only thing I hear about the show until a few years later, when Monica and Greg return from conventions and say they consistently have fans coming up to them to talk about *Ghost Stories*. Fans even have copies of the DVD in their hands, wanting them to sign them. It's all very flattering and I'm really happy that even then, years later, people are still enjoying it.

At the time of *Ghost Stories*, the company is on a roll. We've swelled from 25 employees to 150. We've gone from one rinkydink studio to five full recording suites and two mix rooms. We have two offices in Houston—a headquarters and warehouse, and the recording studio—as well as offices in London and Tokyo. We've been written about in *Entertainment Weekly*, *Forbes*, and the *New York Times*. Our DVDs are selling like gangbusters, and with all the shows we're producing, we're employing over a hundred local actors. The studio enjoys a period of stunning success.

That is until the Great Recession hits and everything goes to shit.

Original line: `What do you think? How does it feel to have the opportunity to become my model? You're lucky. Living is boring. You can only remain beautiful for a short while. After that you crumble and decay. However, now you can have your beauty eternally preserved on this canvas thanks to the hand of this genius.`

Fosterized line: `Oh, I'm sorry, you're the little born again, aren't you? I painted your boss once, he and those twelve dorks he ran with. They wouldn't sit still. After it was all over they stiffed me. Quit moving! Worse than Peter that bastard.`
`Never stopped moving his mouth. Chatty Cathy. "Why do I have to sit next to Judas?" What an apostle.`

Ten Years Later

It's been about a year ago the studio and I parted ways. After being wrecked by bad business decisions and an even worse economy, ADV Films shuttered its doors. Through some crafty maneuvering and sketchy but legal rejiggering, it was reborn as a host of other companies. And those companies became sweatshops. The place I dedicated my life to was killing me. After a few years of working twelve plus-hour days, the studio and I go our separate ways.

One day I get an email from a man who has an anime website; he's looking to do an interview. This is a little strange since I never really gave many interviews when I was in the business, and now that I'm out of the anime racket, it's weird that someone would want to talk with me. When he calls, it becomes clear about halfway through our phone interview that he doesn't know I'm no longer at the studio. When he finds that out, he's thrown, and I offer him a chance to redirect his questions if he wants and we can resume our interview tomorrow. He takes me up on this and we have a very nice chat about my history.

This interview gets picked up by another website and another and then another and by the time I know it, there are headlines like "The End of An Era" and "*Ghost Stories* and The Legacy of Steven Foster." The mood is more *We're gonna miss that guy* than *Glad the bastard's left*—which I am, of course, happy about.

It's about this time that someone sends me a link to a *Ghost Stories* video on YouTube. It's a compilation video by someone named Ilrio, and in it he has cut every joke, every dis, each slam, every pop-culture bomb, and every gag and edited them into three compilation videos called *Ghost Stories Funny Moments 1, 2,* and *3*. In the right column of suggested videos, I see there are also links to entire episodes of the show that have been downloaded to YouTube. Each episode has about three downloads of the same episode, each with respectable view counts. I notice that there are also video reviews of the show. There are even reaction videos of people just watching the show and a camera is recording their responses as they watch the show. Most of the reactions are a hand-to-an-open-mouth and bugged-out eyes. *Oh, shit!* and *Did they just say that?* But it's the first compilation by Ilrio that catches my attention. The video was downloaded ten years ago and the view count is over 300,000. That's not much when divided over ten years, but it's still a respectable number of views. I can't help it, but I'm really flattered by it. And there are several comments to read, all of them wildly complimentary. I make a mental note of this video and decide I'll keep checking on it every once in a while. Soon, something wonderful happens.

I don't know whether it's because of the interview with me and the association of me with the show that brought it to the fore, or what's the reason, but when I check the count the next time, it's up to 450,000 views. So in just a few weeks' time, it's ratcheted up to almost half a million views. In other words, it took ten years for it to get to 300,000 views and now it just took a week or so to get another 150,000. It's like, for some reason, this video is being passed around for everybody to see, now after more than ten years.

When I check it again a few days later, it's up to 500,000! And there are many more comments about it, all of them stellar. I start checking the video almost daily and it gets up to 10,000 views, sometimes more than that, in a single day. I figure if this rate keeps up, it will hit over a million views. Well, the pace not only keeps up, it accelerates. The comments are dizzying in their praise.

"Comedy gold."

"If all anime were like this, I'd watch more anime."

"I'm dead."

"There is no perfect dub for…wait a minute."

"Masterpiece."

"Best dub EVER."

"Steven Foster is a legend/genius/rockstar/etc."

And so on. Plus, the lines are being quoted like mad.

"Think of a big black man chasing you!"

"HaveyouacceptedJesusasyourpersonalsavior?"

"Touch me. Touch me HARDER."

"Ghosts only mess with evil people and Republicans and we're not old enough to vote."

"Just fill the hole, hole filler."

And more.

Every time I log onto my computer, I look at the video to see the count and read the new comments. It's a daily rush. Here it is, the one show that was the most me and it's getting raves from everyone who sees it. Oh, there's one comment every now and then by someone who doesn't like it, but it's like one out of one or two hundred.

It seems like, with a little word of mouth prompted by the one interview I gave, the show begins to reveal itself as this enormous cult hit. I wait for the day when it passes one million. And then it does.

But it keeps going.

Past 1,500,000.

Past 2,000,000.

Past 3,000,000.

Past 4,000,000 views.

Finally, it hits over 4,500,000.

I've been thrilled by this. This little show I put my heart and soul into is now being hailed as a masterpiece. A *masterpiece.* (Italics *mine*!)

It's all too much.

YouTube's taken that and a host of other videos down now—damn algorithm (I guess it was that theme song)—but new ones pop up all the time. "Not because you're a rabbit" has 1,735,889 views, 4,108 comments, and it's a clip of only *one joke*. Just search for "Ghost Stories anime" and you'll find that one and countless others. None of them have a 4,500,000 count but they're still up there.

And when I first came upon that video, I needed to feel good. The last years at ADV had been so horrible that they soured me on my whole sixteen-year career. I found myself not able to look back on any of the good shows, to not see any of the good experiences at all. It started to be like that chapter of my life didn't exist and that was sad. Because I did a lot of good work and had so many good times there.

But when I came across the *Ghost Stories* video compilation, with all its views and all its comments, it caused me to honestly look back on my time with the company and see it for what it was: one of the most fruitful, most accomplished, and most professionally rewarding times in my life.

Now if you had told me that one day something I did would resonate with millions of people, I'd have told you that you were crazy. In my wildest dreams, I never thought I would have something like this. I don't watch any of my old shows or movies. That's another Hollywood myth I thought was true. Believe me, before this, I would have figured I'd be just like Nora Desmond, watching old shows I did, vain and nostalgic. That said, I will occasionally search for a *Ghost Stories* clip if I'm on YouTube. Most of the laughter it brings is because of the way the lines are delivered. That cast was perfect.

The thing that gets me is that I was always afraid to let my freak-flag fly. I thought my flag was *too* freaky. I thought that no one would get me. Or worse, they'd hate me. So I always curtailed myself. I always censored myself. Kept the reins on. But when I let myself go wild, be my 100% complete comedic self, I wasn't just understood, I was embraced. By millions.

So if you're one of those millions who viewed the video, or one of the thousands that commented on it, THANK YOU. You saved my ass. You really did. You probably didn't think anything when you were watching it or commenting on it or quoting lines from the show, but each time you did, there was someone on the other end that was really appreciative of it. And you. Someone that, in a way, needed it. (Keep reading and you'll see how true that is.) You gave me back a part of my life that I had truly lost. I wish there was some way I could thank you for it, I really do.

You shined a light on my past and showed me it gleamed. And that's something I was too in the dark to see.

So whoever you are, if you're ever given the chance, don't be shy. Don't hold back. *Let your freak-flag fucking fly, man.*

There could be a million people out there wanting to sail on your ship.

Or even better, if you're drowning, they may throw you a life saver.

BASKET CASE

The Defender

He is getting ready to lunge at me, as if he is going to break out into a short sprint across the asphalt of the parking lot. I, shockingly enough, am not running. I am not screaming for help. Instead I am shrugging my shoulders, lifting up my arms like Keanu Reeves in *The Matrix*. *Bring it on*. The man looks as though he's going to take me up on it.

Now how did I get here?

I will admit that I was in a little bit of a mood. I was under the gun at work with a production timeline that was just shaved a whole week, which meant I was going to have to record twice as fast, with twice as many actors, in half the time. Making matters worse, the actor that was supposed to show up that night was sick, costing me a precious day that I was going to have to make up somewhere on the back end. The only bright side to this mess was that I was finally able to get out of the studio at a decent hour. I decided to use that time wisely and go to the grocery store. There was nothing at home to eat because I'd been working at the studio, grabbing whatever crappy dinner I could order nearby and wolfing it down between takes. Usually I don't mind grocery shopping, but this was at five in the evening, so it was going to be crowded and I wasn't exactly thrilled at the prospect of waiting in line or wrestling someone for that last bag of romaine.

As I pulled into the parking lot, I saw it wasn't that crowded. The parking lot had a number of cars, but wasn't packed. That's when I saw it. Immediately my neck started to turn to concrete. "It" was a shopping basket, sitting at the intersection of four parking spaces, five spaces away from the corral where someone was *supposed* to put it after they were finished with it.

Now I don't have a lot of pet peeves. Nails on a chalkboard don't bother me. Sure, I get a little agitated when the person in line behind me is so close I can feel their breath on the back of my neck, but I don't go batshit crazy over it. But those shopping baskets? They really get to me.

It's not because I'm concerned about my car getting dinged or anything like that, though you just know it will, with a spread-out herd of free-range shopping carts roaming wild. But that's not what gets me. What makes me mad is the more carts that are left out, the harder it is for those poor guys whose job it is to bring them all back into the store. The task looks like a pain in the ass as it is, having to steer this conga line of wheeled shopping carts, dodging cars that forgot that pedestrians have the right of way. They have to do it in the rain, in the middle of the hottest part of the day, on the coldest days of the year. And, what? Get paid maybe eight bucks an hour? Come on, the least we can do is help 'em out by putting the damn basket in the corral that management constructed for us because we're too lazy to bring the things all that way back in the store. I'm not asking anybody to do that (God forbid), not even if you're just two parking spaces away from the front door. I do wish everybody would take one of those strays out of the parking lot and roll it into the store with you when you first get there to go shopping. But apparently for many people, those leftover carts aren't good enough. The one that's got my ire up this time was the one right at the intersection of four parking spaces. Positioning the cart there was a move that took some real time, time that they could have taken putting it in the cart corral. Drives me nuts.

So I pulled into my space and delicately eased off the brake so my car could edge into the lined box without knocking the cart into the car that's in the space facing me. Or I ricochet the stupid thing and it bounces off that one and then into the one to the left. I threw the car in park, and sighed.

In the row of cars across from me, I notice a couple pushing their grocery basket toward a giant blue F-150 pickup tricked out with special wheels and steel step-ups. With how often Houston floods, that ride was a lot smarter than my low-to-the-ground convertible. Barbie Car, as she's been christened, almost becomes fully submerged in a pothole after a light rain.

A word about my car: I thought convertibles were cool ever since I was a little kid. So I was thrilled when I actually broke down and bought one. At first, I felt like a douche if I put the top down. I didn't want to be *that* guy in his convertible. I was driving away from the studio to go to lunch one day, and when I returned, I ran into Mike, our slick Democrat-hating sales guy.

"I waved to you as you were going to lunch," he said.

"I'm sorry, Mike, I didn't see you."

"I know. You were too busy driving your Barbie car to notice me."

Well, I thought that was the funniest fucking thing I ever heard. So it was Barbie Car from then on. For some reason, that took away any stigma I had about being in a convertible and I put the top down every chance I get. Another reason: when you're at a stoplight and it's a beautiful day and you don't have your top down, people in non-convertibles will yell at you. I know this first hand. So for myself and everybody else, I try to enjoy my convertibleness as much as possible.

At any rate, I turned and went to my trunk to get my reusable grocery bags from Trader Joe's. This was Kroger, so I felt like I was cheating on Joe, adulterous pantry whore that I am.

As I grabbed the bags, the couple near the truck unloaded their groceries and I couldn't help but notice they were about finished with their basket. But I wasn't too worried, their truck was in the space one over from the corral, one empty parking space between them. It's so close, surely, I thought, they're going to put it where it's supposed to be.

Then they didn't.

The girl got into the passenger side of the truck while her linebacker boyfriend just casually shoved the basket into the empty parking space that's RIGHT NEXT TO THE PLACE WHERE YOU'RE SUPPOSED TO PUT THEM. Here it was. I was witnessing the crime while it was actually happening. Without thinking twice, I threw my hands out and shook my head. I glared at him and yelled.

"Really?!"

"What?" he asked. Apparently even his voice took steroids. His girlfriend was now paying attention.

He still didn't get it. (So he was big *and* stupid.) I could have been nice but I'd turned some kind of corner now, there was no stopping me.

"Oh come on, man. It's right *there*! Is it that hard for you to put it in the thing where it's supposed to be or are those two extra steps just too much for you?"

Now he got it. I kid you not, this was his reasoning:

"Hey!" he yelled, jabbing a fat finger in between his two puffy pecs, pointing at himself. "I make a lotta money!"

I couldn't believe it. Did he just actually tell me that because he pulled down a six figure salary, he was entitled to be a douchebag? I yelled back at him, flabbergasted.

"And *that's* your excuse?"

This did not endear myself to him. And now here we are where this story began…

He starts walking toward me. And for some reason, I'm not scared. It's either adrenaline or insanity, but I'm not nervous at all that he's coming to beat the shit outta me. I'm actually kinda nervous for him, as I feel decades of repressed rage coming up from some buried hideout deep within me. This feels like the last straw. This feels like showdown time. Here's where it all comes out. This guy, who by all appearances looks like he could easily kill me, is going to get the full explosion of my fury. I'll snap, just like Ralphie in *A Christmas Story* and this guy will be my Scott Farkus. I'll punch, I'll kick. I'll bite my own shoulder, tear off my right arm, and beat him with it using my left.

So I lean forward, arms out. *Bring it, Motherfucker*!

He gets about four steps. Then he stops. I'm still waiting for him to come. Instead, he waves his hand at me. *Aw, it ain't worth it.* Then he goes around, climbs into his truck while I'm still waiting expectantly, and he drives out of sight.

No beatdown. What a letdown.

Or not.

My bony ass is so filled with righteous anger and justifiable but unpredictable rage, he backed down from me. I challenged a bully and he caved, just like they say they always will, if you were to ever test that little theory like I just did. I am shocked. I am elated. I'm so in love with myself and my terrifying manhood I almost make myself sick. I halfway hope I'd turn around to see another basket offender so I could go after *him*, too. But as I turn around, I see there isn't a basket offender behind me.

Instead, who's standing there is this absolutely gorgeous, young, twentysomething woman, her arms folded over her sizable chest, the last ghost of a frown fading from her face. The only thing her stance is lacking is her foot tapping impatiently. Then it hits me: it wasn't me the guy backed down for. It was because he didn't want this girl to see him act like a dick. Or he didn't want a witness. I don't know. What I do know (now) is that I wasn't the threat. She was.

The girl unfolds her arms.

"That guy was an asshole," she says before walking away.

"Yeah," I mutter, disappointed.

And just for those few seconds, neither was I.

MOONING

The Fool

Lesley Tesh is always called *Tesh!* It's an excitable pronouncement, uttered whenever she is first seen. It's just a thing I do with her. I'm sure she hates it but she puts up with it, as do all other poor bastards I rechristen with a moniker that is more descriptive of their physical or psychic selves than the customary, insufficient name they were given at birth. But I'm the only person who does this, so we'll just call her Lesley for this story. I first met TESH!, or Lesley, at a rock show.

But hasn't everybody?

If you've been to any concert in the Southwest, you've probably seen Lesley Tesh. If you've been to a concert featuring that particular genre of music that is in the metal-god-pantheon vicinity, or any group as famous for their hair as much as their music, then you've definitely seen her. Ninety-nine percent chance you've seen her with her concert-going cohort, also named, oddly enough, Leslie. In a rare showing of restraint, the coincidence gods had the decency to at least have their names spelled differently. Lesley & Leslie are relatively famous on the rock show circuit for being two of the hottest non-groupie groupies to ever—and always—receive the sought-after invite backstage. It's not simply because they're gorgeous, though they are that. It's not that they, pardon the phrase, "put out," because they don't. It's their energy. There is a definite vibration that emanates from their core that causes them to transcend beyond the frequency of Hot Rock Chick. These girls understand the music like musicians do. That's what sets them apart.

Leslie (rebranded as *Sequel* because I met her second) is the raven-haired one of the duo. She possesses a cerebral sexual animus, having the aura of a Zen-tranquil, superhumanly capable tour manager, or a librarian from one of those 80s hot-for-teacher videos. She may eschew the eyewear but her aloof air is so professorial she doesn't need them. A librarian has to take off her glasses to reveal her sexual side. With Sequel, it's with the flip of some internal switch, no discarding of Prada wire frames needed.

Opposite Leslie is Lesley, the fairer of the two, the blonde. She is the Rose Red to Sequel's Snow White. With enormous liquid eyes and voluminous lips, Lesley is more lava-lamp sultry, a seductress shapeshifter. She floats, she blurs, she glides, she envelopes.

Individually, they're relatively normal women. Together, they become this clarion call that turns the ear of every rock guitar player, drummer, and lead singer in the area. Thankfully, this stops them all from playing that unforgettable and obnoxious dun-dun-*dun*, dun-dun-da-*dun*, dun-dun-dun-*da*-dun-dun guitar riff. You know the one, the notes that open "Smoke on The Water," the stoner/rock musician equivalent of "Chopsticks." If there's anything you can count on in rock-n-roll, it's that every stoner knows "Smoke" and that some drunken idiot will shout "Freebird" during a lull in the setlist.

A long time ago, Lesley married one of these rock dudes. A Stone Temple Pilot or a Winger or I don't know who, I don't care. I love earbleed rock as much as the next guy. I would even punish myself gleefully and willfully at a brain-melting My Bloody Valentine reunion, but count me out when there's comps to The Cult or any other band who had Tawny Kataen as a hood ornament. Or any band who simply had Tawny Kataen for that matter. I worship the ground Lesley walks on but when she ultimately turns down that well-worn path toward Head Bangers Ball, I turn atheist, preferring to hang out at Cinderella's—and I mean the Disney chick not the band. We have an unspoken detente about this. She knows I am allowed to pass on the Ratt/Whitesnake double bill and her presence is mandatory at every Garbage concert or St. Vincent appearance. The show where we met was a much more humble affair, just a friend's band playing at a local club, though Lesley's entrance made it rockworthy.

Now my title at the studio is writer-director-producer. In my off hours, I parlay the director position into the role of social director as well, either because I care deeply for the actors and engineers I work with or because I am a megalomaniacal control freak of the highest order.

I host brunches at my house when an actor who has moved away comes back into town for a visit. When one of them is in a play, I organize a gang to go to the theatre and support them. If someone is in the hospital, I wrangle everyone so we can visit our fallen comrade. I send the invites, purchase the flowers, everything I can to make it easier on them because no one likes to visit hospitals. I don't care how much you love the person, going to a hospital is life's second biggest drag, the first one is being the actual person in the hospital. And let me just say that after visiting your loved one who's wasting away from some horrible, incurable disease, when you're drained from the almost impossible task of lifting their spirits, it should be illegal to then charge twenty dollars for parking.

So when Lash (another nickname) and his band, House of Moist, are playing at a local club, I have everyone rally round the fag and come support their friend who has a band with the most revolting name on earth.

This is all happening at the beginning of our company's expansion. Anime is a hot, hot, hot commodity. *Pokémon* Picachu'd their little teeth into the worldwide market, followed by *Dragon Ball Z* fist busting in with *Speed Racer* velocity. Cartoon Network's Toonami block of Japanese anime programming is a staple of the network, one of their prime advertising blocks, soon to be joined by the late night Adult Swim. The studio is selling anime DVDs just as fast as we can dub them into English. Virtually overnight, we grow from one recording suite to five and hire teams to staff them all. Meanwhile, I'm beating the bushes trying to find enough actors to fill all the roles. The studio is blowing up, detonated by the insatiable spark of sudden consumer demand. And there is a price point on it to give the studio incentive to keep cranking them out. An anime DVD with four, maybe five episodes sells retail for around forty dollars—what you'd pay for a whole season of a hit American television show. So it is *ka-ching!* time at work. These are the golden years.

And this night is typical of those times. A grand and gabby group of actors and techies, writers and musicians, hip hangers-on and total strangers, all gathering in a scummy-cool concert bar, everyone with that perfect two-beers-in-you buzz. It's just about then that I become slightly more intoxicated than everyone else—*by* someone else.

The band is tuning up and I'm moving from this group to that, just bouncing around, when I see this *vision* walk into the club and I'm gobsmacked.

"WHO is that?" I ask the person I'm speaking with.

"Oh that's...."

Suddenly they are drowned out by the music supervisor in my head who has cued up "Dream Weaver" just as this gamine walks through the club. She's moving in slow motion like an MTV video shot by Russell Mulcahy. Like Phoebe Cates getting out of the pool.

"...blah blah blah...heard she's a friend of Lonnie's," my informant tells me.

I don't know Lonnie but I know what he looks like and I know he's in Lash's band. My head starts darting around for Lonnie.

The band begins playing.

Now I'm capable of causing a good amount of commotion but not even I can get away with interrupting the opening number to ask the bassist, "Hey, who's this chick that I'm absolutely mooning over? Put down that stupid stringed thing and let's put me and her together."

But I can't take the chance of losing her in the crowd or, worse, she leaves the club altogether. So I start surfing through the mosh pit and get within striking distance. Naturally, my cool demeanor is maintained when I am, at last, upon the poor woman.

"Hi,mynameisStevenandI'msosorrybutwhenIsawyouwalkinthedoorIsawyouandIhadtomeetyou!"

If I was straight, I would get an eye roll and a wave-off. Or slapped. But women forgive this shit from a gay guy. They know immediately the agenda is different. There's no angle. We're totally legit in our non-harassing fawning. Plus, we find everything before the straights, so if we're talking to you before anyone else is, we're your barometer of things to come. You're in, baby. Just ask Madonna. Lady Gaga. Crystal. How "fabulous" became cool and "groovy" was never seen or heard from again.

"Oh.....kay," she tells me, allowing me to hear her voice for the first time. She smiles and rockets explode. Is Lash's band playing? Fuck if I know.

"I'm Lesley," she says loudly but not loud enough. "Lesley Tesh!"

"Nice to meet you, I'm Steven! So you know Lonnie?!"

"Yeah, I've known Lonnie for quite a while," she says. Then she bursts out laughing, like there's some totally hilarious private joke here. I'm not getting it, but I pretend to just so I can watch her laugh. Because there's no sight like a beautiful woman laughing. I'm dazzled. "What do you mean?"

"Oh, you know. You know?"

I answer "No" but my neck is making my head nod "Yes."

More laughter.

"Right, right, gosh, I mean how could you know?" she admits, rolling her eyes. Then she starts laughing again.

Was she just released from prison or something? She's overjoyed with everything. Maybe she's nuts. I don't care.

"You're adorable," I gush. She's so pretty. So happy.

"Oh shut up." Still laughing.

"I mean it. And this is so gonna sound like a line but I need to tell you that I'm a writer and director and I'm working on these Japanese cartoons, dubbing them into English."

"Uh-huh."

Now those big beautiful liquid eyes are scanning me, slightly wary. Maybe it's the anime stigma. Maybe long ago she saw one of those damn shows with tentacles. Because if you think anime is only about finding cute monsters coming out of little orbs, you have no clue what the Japanese can do with squid. And I'm not talking about sushi.

"We're crazy busy," I tell her. I also make sure to clarify my position on octopod-on-human sex in animation. "NON-tentacle anime is huge right now and I am looking…or listening, rather… for more voices. Are you by any chance an actor?" I set the bar lower for her. "Have you ever just acted out?"

Uh-oh. Pretty and Happy is suddenly gone. Replaced by Pretty and…Angry?

What the hell happened? Maybe I'm coming off like a sleazy casting agent.

"Who told you?" She asks, arms folded now, scolding, demanding, suspicious.

"Told me what?" I ask innocently. But it comes out sounding like bad acting. Which is really pissing me off because I *am* innocent. No one told me anything. Hell, *she* hasn't told me anything.

"Come on. Who told you?"

"I swear to God! I really am a director!" I'm trying to get out my wallet and show her a business card or my birth certificate, passport, a skin graft.

"I'm sorry. I just moved back here from L.A." she confesses, embarrassed, coming clean as if we both just realized her profession at the same time. "I thought someone must have told you."

"So you *are* an actor. Excellent!" I say, noticing her beginning to shift her weight from this leg to that.

Wait. We're cool now. Why's she nervous?

"Have you done anything I've seen?" I ask her. "What were you doing out there?"

"Oh, just this stupid show. It's nothing. A series." She doesn't look me in the eyes. What did she do out there? Porn?

"What series?"

"It's just some stupid kids show."

"I have two kids. I probably know it. Come on, tell me."

Then she does that *shmur shmur shmur* thing. You know, how you mumble the answer so no one understands you?

"It ws Pmer Mgers"

"What?" I ask louder.

"Pmer Mgers," she repeats.

"WHAT?"

Then she goes all cartoon on me, making two fists and throwing them down toward the floor, moving her head forward to me slightly, yelling.

"I said *POWER RANGERS*!"

Oh. My. God.

At this time those multi-colored kung fu kids are the hottest thing on broadcast. I'm over the moon.

This woman isn't just an actor—a huge plus all on its own—she's a Power Ranger! My kids are just toddlers. My son, the oldest, could take it or leave it but my daughter loves the show. I've only sat down with her to watch it a couple times but I'm pretty sure there are three...or is it four?...boy rangers and two girl rangers. I vaguely know their faces—gaydar pinged a little bit on the blond with glasses, the Blue Ranger. Still, I couldn't tell you that character's name, the actor's name, nothing. But I definitely know the pink ranger: Kimberly. Because as luck and merchandising tie-ins would have it, McDonald's is giving away Power Ranger action figures in the poisonous but unavoidable happy meals that very summer.

We were on our annual trip to the coast with the 'rents, and I loathed this annual hell. Not because of my family. (Though there are times…) It's just that every year it's the same: The Beach. I hate the beach. Beaches in Texas are disgusting. My first time to see this shit-colored soup in real life was when I was about my kids' age when they first saw it. They didn't seem to care at all while I, when I was their age, was freaking out, wondering how *Hawaii Five-O* could color the water on the TV. I was too young to understand special effects, but I thought they had to have done something. The beach water on TV was brilliant blue green. This water was mud brown. I felt cosmically gypped. When I got older and found out almost every other beach in the world has clear water, it's just Texas beaches that feature brown sludge, I felt even more ripped off. Now I have to spend a week at this sediment swamp every year until the kids go off to college.

But this summer, Zoe has actually won the luck of the draw and, lo and behold, there was a Kimberly in her happy meal.

So there she is, playing in the surf, the disgusting-colored sea mix only about thigh-high on her. I watch her from the virtual living room I've brought down so I can tolerate the day. While I grab vodka, olives, and a martini glass from my own ice chest, I sit at my makeshift bar and watch her play. Her little hands drop down, pink ranger swimming for just a second or two before leaping up, dolphin style. Each time Kimberly dives into the sea, I get nervous. Then each time, thankfully, she'd come up. I need this drink. This is just an accident waiting to happen. Well, sure enough, 3, 2, 1...

"*Kimberly*!" comes the tiny shriek.

I leap over the bar and bolt toward the surf. I'm by my baby's side in seconds, totally quick enough to have saved poor Kimberly but the murky muck of Texas Gulf has clouded any sign of her. So Kimberly is gone, taken out to tide on Crystal Beach, a name that is rage-inducing for its boldface lie.

Oh, the tears. For the rest of the day, Zoe keeps a look on her face that changes from horizon-viewing hope to dusk-approaching depression. We are holding our own toward the end of the day until some idiot with a farmer's tan walks by and, when he is told what happened, says that a fish probably swallowed her. More tears. *Thanks, asshole.*

There my daughter and I sit, living out Otis Redding's most famous song.

But this? This could redeem all that my-father-failed-me feeling I just know Zoe has! No longer will I be the loser who let Kimberly die in a fatal drowning accident. Now I'll be the dad who lost the toy Kimberly but reeled in a real Power Ranger!

"Which one are you?" I ask, looking very much like those bug-eyed anime characters I stare at all day.

"Oh," Lesley demurs. "I'm not a ranger. I'm the girl who runs the juice bar."

The juice bar? Are you kidding me? You're not even the yellow ranger?

I am crushed. And disappointed. For two! I try to hide it but Lesley seems to have noticed. Or maybe she's familiar with this very reaction.

"But just like the rangers have their color, I have a color I always wear," she offers brightly. "Orange."

"Orange. Juice bar," I say. "I get it. My daughter really likes the pink ranger." I ask her to bring in her reel of *Power Ranger* clips with her when she comes in for her audition. She says she will.

Lesley makes good on her promise and brings in a VHS tape. It is impressive. Especially in the episode where the White Ranger, the most heroic of the hued hunks, is wounded on the beach outside the juice bar.

Lesley—yes, in orange—runs forth, chest first. She positions her arms out, Helpless Damsel 101, and stops just short of reaching...

"Tommy!"

Tommy? Juice girl and White Ranger are on a first name basis?

Anyway, it's a big scene but her hands are busy, frozen in damsel mode. She's got to get the other parts of her anatomy to pull off the big moment, all the emotion, the danger, the tension... Tommy could die! Lesley goes at it with busty gusto, delivering the line with not only a Pantene hair-tossing head shake but a matching rack quake as well.

"Look out, White Ranger!" she shimmy/shakes.

Shampoo commercial mane toss + *Airplane!* jello boobquake = we are *done*.

The group watching, a good six or seven of us, howl with laughter when we see this little cheesecake scene *in a children's show* and I've never seen a tape ejected so fast in my life. Lesley storms off, playfully pissed.

"Fuck y'all! Fuck all y'all," she tells us, walking down the hall of studio row, middle finger raised high. The finger lingers in midair for emphasis, even after her body's turned and disappeared around the corner. Then her hand vanishes and we hear her voice coming back toward us, echoing up the hall. "I saved Tommy's life!"

So ever since that House of Moist show, Lesley and I have been pals. She's moved to Austin now, but she still comes down to record. Often she'll come down to visit her father whose health is failing and we'll see each other then. Or when she can squeeze me in between bands she and Leslie would be headbanging to.

Lesley's marriage to that Creed Temple Jam dude might not have lasted but that wasn't the last of her romances with rock stars. Years later, she runs into a guitar player she was friends with in high school. They decide to get together and talk about old times when, at the end of their visit, they're both sitting in his car and they look at each other.

"I love you," she tells him.

"I've loved you since high school," he replies.

The next thing I know I'm getting a picture of Einar the guitar player (now husband), her daughter from the previous marriage, and Lesley, all in a white vista of Canadian snow. Lesley looks beautiful, a little like Emma Frost, dressed in a white coat and ushanka hat, married and...pregnant.

Fortunately/unfortunately this all starts happening as Einar has signed on to be the guitar player in Kelly Clarkson's band, just as Clarkson is settling into another white-hot phase of her career, selling out stadiums, slaying on *SNL*, and taking the occasional fat-cash corporate gig. It's rough on the newlyweds, but Einar's doing what he loves with one of the best pop singers in the world. Bonus points: Clarkson is just as nice and down-to-earth as you'd think she is. Since Lesley lives in Austin now, I don't get to see her as often as I used to, so when I do it's a treat.

And copious amounts of liquor are consumed.

One night, both Leslie and Lesley are at my house after having saki and sushi. Admittedly, I have more of the prior and less of the latter and suggest that, instead of wasting a good buzz, why not continue our evening at my place and share a bottle of wine?

Well, one chardonnay and one velvety cab later, I'm certainly feeling no pain.

Lesley's telling us all about her life and she happens to mention that Einar is in New York that very night playing Madison Square Garden for two sold-out shows with Kelly Clarkson as she double bills with Reba McEntire. Sequel then gives us the 411 of her world. I update them on various bits of studio drama and the usual skinny. Speaking of skinny...

"You look *really* good," Lesley tells me, out of the blue.

Immediately, I'm thrilled anyone's noticed.

"*Power 90*!" I declare, flexing.

Yes, that infomercial they run at three in the morning got to me and I ordered *Power 90*. I will admit to you as I did to them that I have never made it past disc one of the six-disc set but, hey, for me that's something. A vodka on the rocks is pretty much the only heavy lifting I really enjoy doing. That said, somehow I've come to enjoy this practice and between *Power 90*, the running, and the *Men's Health Belly Off Diet* my bony bod has experienced a nice little makeover. I am close to achieving hunk status.

So naturally, every time I see some hot guy in my house only to realize that it's me in the mirror, it's a reminder to take a selfie. This has gotten out of hand, I'll admit. Every time I change clothes, it turns into such a production you'd think Steve Miesel was gonna show up with Grace Coddington. If I had hair I would have to buy a wind machine. Disgusting.

The most astonishing area of my new hot bod is my bony ass. At last, after all these years, I have junk in said trunk. I'm ridiculously proud of myself and my achievement.

Now I'm not drunk enough to drop trou but I *am* loaded enough to whip out one of the more impressive pics from the portfolio I have on my iPhone and show both Lesley and Sequel a shot of my perfectly sculpted ass. Naked, of course.

They are just drunk enough to think this is hilarious as well. It is about this time that Einar, Lesley's husband, texts in.

"I thought he was playing the Garden?" I ask for clarification. I look at the kitchen clock and, while a bit blurry, I know it isn't any later than eleven.

"They just finished. He's on the way to the hotel."

"Madison fucking Garden. I'm going to moon him."

In my head, this makes perfect sense.

Lesley agrees this is a splendid idea and gives me his number. I send the pic waiting for the LOL reply.

Moments fly by. The reply never comes. We go back to talking until Lesley's phone buzzes. She looks at the text and reads a very long time and after she's finished reading, she starts laughing.

"What? Why are you laughing?" I demand to know. "Did I get a bad review?"

"Ah, no," Lesley says, those damn lips of hers curling into a Cheshire grin that could only be more unnerving if it was coming from her just-now disembodied head.

"What's it say?" I ask, now nervous.

Sequel has already sidled up next to Lesley and whatever the message says she finds it equally riotous.

"Read it, goddammit!"

Lesley clears her throat and begins reading. "Hilarious. We needed that."

A question pops into my quickly sobering head: *We?* She continues.

"Tell Steven that Kelly thinks he's got a great ass."

"What?!"

The blood is draining from my head, only to rush back up there to turn my face bright red. Lesley begins to read what has transpired since the picture in question was sent.

Apparently, Einar receives the picture and immediately explodes into laughter. Kelly Clarkson happens to be passing by him as *they are all on the bus together* and inquires as to what Einar is laughing about. Kelly Clarkson is then showed the picture. So, in essence, I didn't just flash Einar, I mooned Kelly Clarkson.

If this isn't humiliating enough, now Reba fucking McEntire wants to know what's so funny so the phone is passed to Reba. Clearly Reba is not prepared for this and is mighty flustered by a shot of a perky round bubble butt. Einar goes on to explain that Reba is usually one cool customer, that her tour runs like a Tag Hauer. So for them all to see Reba this flustered is a thrill for everyone. Reba McEntire then, however, confirms what Kelly Clarkson has said about my now-public behind—it's pretty great—and they all have a good laugh. At my expense.

"You dumbass, they're all on the bus together. They take the bus to the hotel," Lesley tells me, as if I am accustomed to how rock stars get across town. For all I know they could take the soul train.

"Kelly Clarkson thinks you have a hot ass," smiles Sequel.

"Shut up!" Honestly, I'm mortified.

I mean, it's Kelly Clarkson. It's not like Courtney Love or anything. Hell, I could have posed like Mapplethorpe's notorious whip photograph for Courtney Love and it wouldn't have phased her.

"Well what did you think was going to happen? That he'd just shrug and 'whatever.' You sent him a picture of your..."

"Butt." Sequel finishes the sentence for her. "I think the term you're looking for is BUTT."

"You can shut up."

They're both howling at all this and all I'm thinking is now I know how Elliot Spritzer feels. But then, just as I'm about to rake myself over the coals for being so stupid, I spot the silver lining in all this.

Even Kelly Clarkson thinks I have a nice ass.

I will note that, shortly after all this transpired, Kelly Clarkson married her husband. You, of course, are seeing the obvious connection here, yes? I was an aphrodisiac for the woman and she immediately married her boyfriend so she wouldn't cheat on him! *Duh*. Unfortunately, Reba divorced her husband shortly thereafter. Take from this what you will.

The moral of this story is that when you meet someone, you never know where that relationship will take you. One moment, you're fawning over a girl in a nightclub and before you know it you are mooning pop stars and breaking up marriages.

It's a short, slippery slope from starstruck to stupidity.

Me? I know that slide all too well.

Me. And my ass.

MARVEL, US

The Father

THE PLAY IS ALWAYS THE SAME. THE CHILDREN WAKE ME UP, TINY hands tugging at the sheet and blanket, or the neck or sleeve of my T-shirt, little faces smiling. They're always happy in the a.m. That's because every morning they wake up it's like the first morning they've woken up. Everything from last night is all new again in the morning. What's not to be happy about? And you're the only person they really know, so they're always eager to see you.

Despite the early hour, I wake up quickly, fully alert. It's something that happens to you after you have children. You sleep with your third eye open. Their mother likes to sleep late, so I slip out of bed and the kids and I—ages three, two, and twenty-eight, respectively—pad down the stairs to the kitchen.

I plop them down near my feet as I start to make breakfast. They're too short to reach pan handles yet, so it's still a safe zone. And I'm pretty good with the eggs, bacon, etc. that they have minimal risk of being hit by a dropped egg or a slippery piece of pork. The oven's a bit dicey, with the biscuits and the hot baking sheet, but they've wandered away by that time. Soon breakfast is ready; I plate it up and take their dishes to the living room where they are already seated in front of the television in anticipation of the upcoming show. And it's not quite the one you're probably thinking.

I don't use the TV as a babysitter really. Watching television with them is a more interactive, less passive pastime than dully staring at the screen with wide but vacant eyes. And I time this so that their breakfast is finished by the time the show starts.

We're wasting time with whatever cartoons are on before the appointed hour. But right at ten, the channel turns to Fox to watch *X-men*. *X-men* is a cartoon based on Marvel's team of mutant superheroes. I'm not a nerd. Not really. Comics didn't hold any special place on my bookshelf when I was a kid. To me, they were just like any other book I read. But this comic-based show gets me, with its themes of tolerance and acceptance. I know the concepts are above their little heads right now but I like to think that some sort of morality osmosis is occurring, even if that's as subtle as a fragrance holding onto fabric.

They love this show, mostly because of the opening title sequence. After a recap of last week's episode, the animated opening begins with each member of the X-men getting their own share of introductory screen time. Their names zoom onto the screen one by one and then each X-man performs a signature move in keeping with their own special power or gift. Cyclops is first, his eyes blasting a crimson beam skyward. Then the screen wipes clean and Wolverine follows, slashing his adamantium claws before slicing the image away, camera left. And so on.

This animated sequence becomes a much more active, 4-D experience when the kids are watching with me. They don't just watch the cartoon. They *are* the cartoon.

I'll have one of them sitting on my lap and the other will be nearby, waiting eagerly. When the music starts and the titles begin, I reach my hands under their shoulders and, within a flash, they're airborne. I then hurl them whichever way the animated character is going, mirroring the action onscreen. If Gambit jumps forward, so does Sam. If Storm flies onto the screen tossing lightning, so does Zoe. My son weighs less than forty pounds, so it's nothing for me to keep him off the ground, spinning in the air, leaping, lurching. My two-year-old daughter is even lighter, so I practically perform a mini Cirque du Soleil with her in my arms. I scamper her up the wall of the living room, moving her little legs like Peter Parker. (Yeah, yeah, I know. He's not an X-man. But he's still Marvel. It's not like I compared him to a DC character or anything. Chill.) The air fills with the sound of the synthesizer-heavy theme song and the laughter of two toddlers. It is the finest music to hear and some of the most fun I've had in my life. I make them move like superheroes, but to them, *I* am a superhero.

After the titles are finished, they both crawl back into my lap, one on each folded leg, and we sit on the floor before the television set and watch the rest of the show. We see the mutants persecuted, then they fight for their right to be, a tidy little moral is learned (Prejudice is bad. Acceptance good.) and then it's all over in twenty-something minutes plus commercials. And if I'm bored, even these get an acrobatic accompaniment. But I totally dig the X-men.

These mutant overachievers (or victims; your power can be a gift or it can more closely resemble a curse) are born with a mutant X gene. And then, usually around puberty, the mutation presents itself and you can suddenly absorb people's life force or become the latest cover model for *Telekinesis Weekly*. There is no "cure" for the X gene. You're born with it. God doesn't make mistakes. Yada yada yada. You know where this is going, don't you?

My kids are, like I said, far too young to understand the symbolism. But that doesn't stop me from explaining the themes of the cartoon to them. I address them like a toddler congress.

"So if someone is different than you, don't be mean to them or anything like that," I tell them as they stare at me like everything I say is some magical incantation. (I *love* toddlers.) "You share your toys with them and play with them as you would any other little boy or girl. Being different is no crime. In fact, what makes you different can be what makes you special. It also means you should probably vote Democrat, but you can figure that out when you get older." I never said my lectures to them would be bipartisan.

But very quickly, they return their starry-eyed gazes to the screen, presumably forgetting everything their pedantic dad just told them. But this message resonates deeply within me. Probably more than I like to admit.

I am a married man and closet homosexual. My childhood was steeped in a religion that pretty much taught me I was going straight to hell for affections I couldn't help. The fear of that punishment, and a desire to be right with The Man Upstairs, steered me toward a wife and family. The perfect heteronormative unit. But it's a mask I can't keep wearing. It erodes a little more every day. No matter how much I try to deny it or keep it buried. It is just a matter of time before I take this perfectly nice little household and rip it to shreds, explode it from within. So I cherish these mornings with the kids deeply. The turmoil inside me has not yet erupted into the house; the contents haven't spilled over to sully them in their baby-scented pajamas. But soon. Soon everything will change. And no superhero is coming to stop it. No superman is going to save them from what is about to happen. The villain? It's their own father.

* * *

They are older now. It has been four years since their mother and I divorced, and the kids, thankfully, at this young age have taken the transformation of one home into two in stride. Me? I'm not doing so well. Liberation has come at a high price and I pay it every moment the kids aren't with me. I get them the customary one weeknight for dinner and every other weekend. My ex-wife has moved far from my inner-city home. Depending on the traffic on any given day, the round trip to pick them up, bring them to my place, then deliver them back to their mother takes me two to three hours. So our Tuesday night dinners give us barely enough time to eat before I have to take them home again. And weekends, I get gypped. My wife shrewdly put it in the divorce decree that I would be responsible for pickup and drop-off. I should have been suspicious when she had the mileage parameter changed as well. But I never dreamed she would move the children to another city. I know she was angry, but I didn't know she was that mad. Not furious enough to use the kids like that. But she and I barely get along at all now, a state made even worse by the fact that she got remarried. And that wouldn't bother me if it wasn't *who* she married.

Our marriage therapist.

I know what you're thinking. And, yes, it is crazy but, no, it's not against the law. It is unethical, I think. And weird. I mean he, more than anyone, knew how screwed up she was when he married her. But he's a religious zealot who shares her fundamentalist beliefs to a T so they're perfect for each other. The kids receive their daily dose of Old Testament and Jesus, made worse by the fact that she plans on homeschooling the kids and I have no power to stop her. I give them a countering dose of a more accessible form of religion every time they're with me. My prayer is that with their mother being so far right and my being extreme left, the kids will walk a perfect line, straight down the middle. They'll be perfectly balanced, not fucked up like their furious parents. It's a foolish hope. But it's my hope.

I spend most of my days drinking. The emotional price of the divorce was high. And I'm living in squalor since I gave her the car, the house, everything so that the kids wouldn't suffer. Well, they wouldn't suffer as much as I could help it. And even though they're young, they've been impacted. I don't think they're old enough to miss me as much as I miss them. Their arms, thankfully, don't ache like mine do, these ghost arms that used to joyfully carry children in them and now that joy is relegated to court-ordered days and strictly adhered-to nights. I drive as fast as I can to go get them and as slowly as possible to return them. The trip alone back to my house is usually tear-filled and I can't wait to get home to have a drink to numb the pain. The sauce is my solace. I joylessly pick up toys and put them away. I fold little outfits as I drown in melancholy. I count the days until the next time they'll be mine again.

When they're with me, it's a nonstop party. It's twenty-four-hour-a-day play. If I happen to sleep late because I stayed up too late the night before, I leave a trail of colorful notes from their bedroom to the kitchen where there is a tower of individual cereal boxes waiting for them. But most mornings I'm up with them, making breakfast and squeezing every moment I can out of the time.

I'm out of the crappy post-divorce apartment I moved into. Now I have a boyfriend who loves the kids and we live in a modest but nice two bedroom house in a quaint, established neighborhood. The kids have a room with bunk beds in it; there are toys that stay at my house and clothes that stay at my house (my ex refuses to pack them an overnight bag) and all the childhood supplies I need to make their stay at my house as appointed as the home they share with their mother. Although I can't compete with the two-story mansion on a golf course that she now lives in, I do have a pool with a rock waterfall, which more than makes up for the deficit in living space. They're too young for golf anyway.

The pool gets used every weekend. It is the background to most of our play. The rock waterfall is built with flat stones, water traveling through the shelving and gaps the stones create—perfect for X-men figures to flow through and into the pool proper. This provides hours of entertainment for the kids, though they usually make me act out all the characters except their solo favorites. It's exhausting being a whole cast, but I enjoy it. I play the good guys, the bad guys, the attack blasts and explosions of battle. I make pretty good sound effects and I'm animated enough to keep things interesting. Probably too interesting as "our" play usually devolves into my performance art for an audience of two. But, oh the big adventures we have.

These are called, by the children "abigaventures" and they request such every time I'm with them. The abigaventures can happen anywhere. The pool is not our only shooting location. The abigaventure takes place in the front yard. It happens in the driveway, a caravan of vehicles and dolls snaking down the chalk-graffitied concrete. It goes down inside, mostly centered around the coolest modern doll house known to man. It's not actually a doll's house but rather a contemporary miniature home where there are small Eames chairs, little Florence Knoll sofas, and tiny versions of pieces by Eero Saarenin. It's a two-story house with walls made of clear, colored plexiglass that can be taken out of their various slots and re-slotted so that the house is an ever-changing kaleidoscope of contemporary cool. That's what it's called: The Kaleidoscope Doll House. I found it at the Contemporary Art Museum in New York. It did come with the stock nuclear family—father, mother, daughter, son—but these have been pushed to the side and the structure is command central for the X-men figures that, as if designed to, fit perfectly into every designer chair and sofa and pass easily through the thin hallways lined with tiny replicas of Edvards Munch and Hopper. I found the house online and got it for my daughter one Christmas, though she and my son share it without selfishness. The house is ground zero for most abigaventures' beginnings. These action extravaganzas also happen, of course, at the pool.

The X-men don't fit as snugly and perfectly in Barbie's Dream Van but that doesn't stop them from using it as transport through the backyard "jungle." Because abigaventures always happen in a jungle.

This jungle is even cooler because it's right near a giant lake, aka the swimming pool. The X-men prepare for their grand assignment, and as is always the way with these things, the mission goes terribly awry, and the X-men are plunged into peril. They must defeat an assault by the various bad guys; favorite among them is a man/pterodactyl creature called Sauron with large flapping green wings on his clawed arms. The X-men are all piled into the Barbie van and then the van is sped right into the pool, its full-sided hinged panel then forced open with the impact of the water and the X-men explode into the pool, some floating, some sinking, depending on the type of plastic and amount of air the figure can hold to keep it buoyant. We do have a few token Barbies along for the ride but mainly they're just there because their hair looks cool underwater—as the kids see because they often view this terrible crash from underneath, while wearing goggles over submerged, enlarged eyes.

It's all great fun and keeps them entertained for almost a good hour and then it's time for they themselves to play in the pool while the figurines dry in the summer sun. Occasionally there will be the authentic kind of drama with one missing hero but he's usually found sucked onto the screen over the pool drain or one of the skimmers. Then, after they're dry, they're all packed up again and placed in their badass multicolored command center until the weekend after next, when the kids come to play with them again.

Evenings are filled with baths and bedtime stories. Most meals are home cooked. Because I know their mother is alien to the kitchen and healthy eating, I cram as many vitamins and nutrients into their little bodies as I can in a forty-eight-hour timeframe. In the divorce, she took the McDonald's and I got saddled with four squares. But I spoil them in other ways, if not junk food. We shop for clothes and toys and I refuse them almost nothing. And so far, they've skirted selfish or spoiled brat territory. They're both really good kids. They get along with each other well and never fight.

There's rarely a complaint and they're remarkably well-behaved. They carry themselves with such sweetness that when my boyfriend and I are invited to a party on a weekend we have the kids, we'll dress them up and take them with us. And they behave flawlessly. Maybe this going down the middle thing isn't so farfetched after all.

That is until…

* * *

"Boys marry girls and girls marry boys."

This announcement comes from my daughter sitting in the back seat. I know where this is coming from. Jesus camp. I've grown to hate fundamentalists. So I fight back with as much brainwashing as I get confronted with.

"Not necessarily, Zoe," I tell her.

"That's what Mommy says."

"Well, sometimes boys marry boys and girls marry girls." I scan my brain for a pertinent example she will understand. It comes, of course, from the toys. "It's like if Rogue liked Storm. She could marry Storm if she wanted to. And they're both girls."

"Could Cyclops marry Gambit?" my son asks.

"If they're in love. But I think Cyclops is hooked up with Jean Grey."

Zoe holds the Jean Grey card. Sam's got Cyclops.

"Zoe, give me Jean Grey," he demands.

"Sam, you can have Jean Grey when Zoe's not playing with her. They can be married and still not hang around each other all the time. It happens." I start to panic as my example starts unraveling due to property ownership.

"I don't want Jean Grey to marry Cyclops," Zoe pleads.

"She doesn't have to. Marriage happens when two people love each other and they want to spend as much time together as they can. If Jean Grey wants to play the field, she can."

"What's 'play the field' mean?" she wants to know.

"It means she could hook up with Wolverine if she wants to," I tell her, realizing this is a thing in the X-men universe. "She has the hots for him anyway. So I don't think she's going to marry Cyclops anytime soon."

Is this working? I feel like it's working.

"You follow all that?"

"Yes," they both say and I wonder if they're just wanting me to shut up.

So I shut up. For now. But with two inquisitive kids, that's not going to last long.

Case in point:

"Dad?"

"Yes, Sam?"

"Can I take the X-men book to Mom's house?"

I hate having things go to their Mother's house. They never, ever make it back.

"You don't want to keep it at my house?"

"No, I want to read it at my house."

"Okay."

I wish I could have seen it coming that this was a bad idea.

I drop the kids off and make the long drive back home. After I get back to my house, I'm not there thirty minutes and the phone rings. I answer and find out that it's Lloyd, my ex-wife's new husband and my old marriage therapist.

"Steven, it's Lloyd."

Hey, you fuck head is what I want to say. But instead I make nice.

"Hey, Lloyd. Is everything alright? The kids okay?"

"Yes, they're fine. But I wanted to talk to you about the book Sam brought home."

The *X-men* book?

"What about it?" I ask suspiciously.

"Well, there is witchcraft in the book and we don't have things like that in our home."

Witchcraft? What the hell is he talking about? I've read that book like forty times already. There's no spell in any of those pages.

"What are you talking about?"

"Well," he begins. "They have powers and that's not real. It's like a form of magic. And magic is satanic. And we don't allow that in our house."

Immediately, my blood temperature rises about twelve degrees.

"Where's the book, Lloyd?" I ask him flatly. With maybe a touch of menace.

"I threw it away."

"You what?"

"I threw it away."

My son loves that book. Papa Bear shows up.

"Look, Lloyd," I say. My voice is quiet but loaded. "That book's not satanic. It's a comic book. And if you ever throw one of my kids' books or toys or anything in the trash again, I'm going to drive up to that house and I'm going to bust open that door and I'm going to pull you outside the house and I'm going to beat the living shit out of you on that golf course." I don't realize it but I've raised my volume with each sentence I've said. By "golf course" I'm practically screaming. "You got that, Lloyd?"

He starts to say something. I cut him off.

"And you know I'd fucking do it, too, Lloyd," I hiss. "Now put Annie on the fucking phone."

I hear him put the phone down and call my ex-wife's name in the background. Within a moment, she's picked up the phone.

"What?" she asks tersely.

Fine.

"Look, Annie. If Lloyd *ever* pulls another stunt like that again, I'm going to come up there and beat the shit out of him. What *the fuck* were you thinking letting him get away with something like that?"

"He's my husband, Steven."

"And I'm the kids' father. That trumps anything that fucking *Lloyd* wants to do. You got that?" I'm shaking I'm so angry. "Now if you have a problem with the book, that's your issue. But you don't throw something of his that I got him away. *Ever*. Now you're going to go to that trash can and you're going to fish that book out of the goddamn trash and you're going to keep it until I pick up the kids on Tuesday. You don't have to read it to them. You don't have to give it to them. But you're damn sure going to give it back to me. And if I say he can have a book about the fucking X-men or any letter men, he's going to have it. Am I real fucking clear about this?"

"You don't have to use that kind of language with me," she says.

"Am I real fucking clear about this?"

There's a pause. Then a sigh.

"Yes," she says.

"Good. Now put Sam on the phone."

"He's in bed."

"Then take the phone to his fucking bed."

"Just a minute," she says and there's a long pause. I sit down at my dining room table and just *vibrate*.

Soon, my son is on the phone.

"Sam?"

"Yes, Dad?"

"So I hear there was a problem with your book."

"Lloyd said I shouldn't read it."

"Well, son, if Lloyd doesn't like it, he doesn't have to read it. But he's never going to take away something of yours again. Do you understand me? That was a mistake. And your mom is going to get the book out of the trash and we're going to take it back to Daddy's house. And we're going to read that book just like we always have, you hear me? There's nothing wrong with that book. And there's nothing wrong with you for wanting to read that book."

Silence.

"Do you hear me, Sam?"

"Yes, Dad."

"Okay, good. Now go to sleep and have sweet dreams, son. Dream about X-men if you want to. You dream about whatever you want. Now I love you. I'll see you on Tuesday."

"I love you too, Dad."

"Goodnight, Sammy."

"Goodnight, Daddy."

I hang up the phone. My heart's still racing. My mind is racing. I'm still furious. I think about my son in his bed, the confusion that must be going through his mind. I'm enraged to think he might feel any shame, or that he's done something wrong. I hate being a divorced dad. Divorced dads get screwed. When I started to divorce my wife, the first thing I did was speak to a lawyer about getting custody of the kids. I knew what I was going to hear, but deep down I was hoping I wouldn't. Connie Moore was a well-respected lesbian attorney (she's passed now) who specialized in family law. She was recommended by a good friend of mine and I figured she'd be the one to ask about the possibility of my getting custody of my children. She was gracious and kind, but not encouraging.

"Steven," she told me, "I feel for you, I really do. But this is Texas. And no judge in the state of Texas is going to give a gay father custody over their birth mother. I'd love to tell you something different, but that's just not the case. I've even seen cases where they've given an unfit mother custody over the father. A straight father."

"Can I try it?" I asked her, the hope in my head dwindling but the hope in my heart holding on for dear life.

"Of course. You can try anything. But I'm telling you that more than two decades of experience in this area of the law and experience in the Texas courts, the chances of you winning custody are incredibly slim."

She was not only kind enough to tell it to me straight; she didn't charge me a dime for her counsel. Small consolation. Microscopic, really.

After the phone call, I sat there and thought about the injustice of it all.

Meanwhile, back at my house, I still rage. Then I stand up, get in my car, and drive to the closest comic book store.

"I'm looking for *X-men* comic books," I say to the clerk.

"Sure. What issue?"

"All of them."

* * *

They've been in there a long time. My daughter and my friend Mona, a photographer. Mona needed models and asked if she could shoot my daughter and I, of course, told her yes. It means free, artsy photographs of my kids (my son would also be shot, even if he wasn't the primary subject for the project). I told her she could shoot them as much as she wanted to if it meant pro bono portraits. They've never been professionally shot before, so I'm concerned my daughter might not take to this whole modeling thing. After all, she's only a child. Eventually, Mona comes out of the spare bedroom, where they've been taking the pictures.

"Well?" I ask her. "How's it going?"

"You should be very proud," Mona says. Then, gravely: "And very nervous."

"Why nervous?"

"Take a look."

She holds up the camera and, with her finger, turns the wheel on the back so images roll by and I'm able to see the whole photo shoot from its beginning.

From like, the third picture, Zoe's already relaxed in front of the camera. And she only gets better from there. She looks pensive. Sad. Beatific. Angelic. Haunting. And in more than a few photographs, unnervingly alluring. It's a little disconcerting when a five-year-old is giving the camera what looks to be a "come hither" look. It's not kiddie porn by any stretch, but she's definitely in Sally Mann territory.

"That freaks me out."

"You're gonna have your hands full."

"Thanks," I tell her flatly. Then my daughter rolls up. I bend over and scoop her into my arms. "Did you have fun?"

"Yes. Can I go play now?" she wants to know.

"Of course."

"You play with me."

"Alright."

I look over to the living room floor where my son is playing a game, X-men figures strewn about, no longer the focus of either of their play as they once were. My daughter squirms in my arms to get down. Still, I don't let her down just yet. My arms keep her held tight. Because they won't always be able to do so. I turn to Mona.

"You ready for Sam?"

"Yeah. I'm finished with Zoe. I got more than enough. It'll be hard to cull."

"I don't wanna talk about it." I turn to Sam. "Hey, buddy. You ready to get your picture taken?"

"Yeah!" he says. Mona showed him a gold mask earlier and told him he would be wearing it in one of the pictures so he's excited.

Perfect. I've got one daughter who's ready to go cover of child *Vogue* and another waiting for his shot to land cover on *Esquire*.

Zoe and Sam will later be shot by another photographer. Her work is saturated, blurry color whereas Mona's was stark black and white. These images, too, are incredibly striking, dramatic. Shots of the children in the attic. Out back on a swing. Sitting on a vintage suitcase in the tall grass. They look like lost angels, little vagabonds.

Sam will eventually lose interest in this whole scene. Zoe will go on to be signed by the biggest modeling agency in the Southwest. But she has been spoiled by just one photographer each time working with her. When she gets her first gig for a catalogue shoot, she freaks out and changes her mind about this modeling business. Too many people running around, too many people pushing and pulling at her. Too-bright lights, too many flashing strobes. She finishes the shoot but announces she's retiring from modeling, though not in so many words. They're more like, "Daddy, I don't want to do this again."

I mourn the chance at getting her college tuition paid for with a nice long modeling career before she turns ten, but alas, it's not meant to be.

* * *

It's Sam's turn in the bath. Zoe has gone first and I have her out now, dressed in her pajamas, her hair still damp. I place her on the king bed in front of the television. She sits there holding her latest acquisition, a small, stuffed, floppy pink unicorn named Sparkle. The two have been inseparable since Sparkle's addition to the household.

Sam's old enough to bathe himself, so after turning off the water, I leave him alone and go into the kitchen to begin cleaning up the dishes after dinner. My boyfriend is in the living room, reading the newspaper. All is quiet. Then:

There's a loud thud, followed by a bloodcurdling scream.

David throws his paper down; I throw the dish in my hands into the sink, shattering it, and both of us run to our bedroom.

There, we see Zoe, laid out on the floor by a bunched-up rug. Immediately, we realize what has happened: Zoe has jumped off the bed and, when she landed on the rug, it slipped out from under her. And she went down hard, face first. She's screaming bloody murder and I quickly bend down to pick her up.

When I raise her head, I see it. Blood is flowing like a small stream from her chin, which is split open so wide I can almost see her jawbone. She's wailing and I'm surprised I'm not panicking. Instead, I immediately switch into Producer Mode, holding her and hushing her and telling her she's going to be alright, that I'm here, that she's fine.

Producer Mode is something that happens when the shit's hitting the fan. I'm familiar with this setting. Suddenly, you are The Man With All The Answers. The Man Who Can Do Anything. You speak in quick, efficient sentences. You analyze everything. You deduce what the best course of action is. You take on tasks you've never done before. Your blood pressure doesn't raise in the slightest. Years of training has ingrained this behavior into me. I don't switch it on. It comes on immediately, on reflex. Things get *done* when you're in Producer Mode.

I look at David.

"Get Sam out of the bath," comes the calm, clipped order. He bolts to the bathroom.

I'm still holding and rocking Zoe. I stand up with her in my arms and move her toward the bathroom.

"David, throw me a hand towel."

He does.

I take the towel and gently hold it to her split, bleeding chin. Tears have streamed down her face to her jawline and the water mingles with the flowing blood.

"We gotta take her to the hospital."

"I'll get Sam dressed," David says.

Within seconds, Sam is dressed and Zoe is wrapped in a blanket. David opens the car door for Sam and he scurries inside.

"Is Zoe going to be alright?" he wants to know.

"She's going to be fine, Sam," I tell him. "You're going to be fine, Zoe."

I don't know if she's going to be fine.

Luckily, David realizes there's a hospital emergency room just a few miles from our house. We speed there, Zoe's screaming acting like a siren the entire way. We pull up to the ER door and I jump out of the car with Zoe in my arms.

"You bring Sam, I'll meet you inside," I say as I run.

Zoe and I enter the ER, my head darting this way and that for someone to talk to, someone to yell at. I find a nurse almost immediately. Now that there are people here to handle the situation, Producer Mode shuts off and I'm just your average, run-of-the-mill, hysterical parent.

"It's my daughter, she split her chin wide open! I think she needs stitches!"

"Let me see," the nurse says and comes over to Zoe. Gently, she takes the soaked hand towel from her face. "Ooh, yes. We better get her looked at right away. This way, Mr…?"

"Foster. I have someone with me, he can check us in. I'll go with you."

While the nurse speaks to other staff members, David comes walking in with Sam.

"Here's my insurance card, just take care of everything for me. Zoe and I are going with her," I say.

"I'll watch Sam. We'll be right here. Go," my boyfriend says.

The nurse returns.

"This way, Mr. Foster," she is all-business with me, 100% Mother Goose with Zoe. "What's your daughter's name?"

"Zoe."

"Zoe, my name is Lanisha. We're going to take care of you, honey."

Zoe's either exhausted herself or distracted by the hospital cacophony, but she's growing quieter.

"That's a pretty horsey you have there. What is that? Wings? Does she have wings?"

Zoe nods, her face wet with tears and blood.

"Well, you hold onto her, Zoe. We'll let her go with us to see the doctor. He's going to fix you right up, sweet baby."

I'm nodding and repeating everything the nurse says like an idiot. I was so cool and in control at the house, but now with another person on the case I'm reverting to a babbling moron.

Shortly a doctor appears, and after making a quick introduction, he examines her.

"Yes," he says calmly, "she's going to need stitches. We'll give her an injection that will numb the area. Then we can stitch her up. She's going to be fine."

"You hear that, Zoe? The doctor says you're going to be fine."

"I…don't…want…stitches," she cries. She doesn't even know what stitches are, but even she can tell she doesn't want them. It's like kids instinctively know doctors may claim to be healers, but first they're hurters. They stick sticks down your throat and needles in your arm. Suckers afterward are weak compensators.

"Now, Mr…?" the doctor says, just like the nurse before him.

"Foster. This is Zoe."

"Mr. Foster, I'm afraid you're going to have to hold her during the procedure. Now we're going to wrap her very tightly in that blanket to curtail her movements, but she's going to want to move. Your job is to limit that movement as much as you can while I quickly stitch up the wound. Do you understand, Mr. Foster?"

Yes, I'm going to be having to hold my daughter down while you attack her with a needle and thread. Got it. Thanks for that.

"I understand."

The team begins prepping and I rock Zoe back and forth in my arms. She's calmer now. Before the storm.

"The doctor's going to take good care of you, Zoe. And I'll be here the whole time."

I half expect her to ask for her mother, but she doesn't. She just clamps onto my sleeve and leans into me like she won't ever let go. Soon, the doctor and nurse are ready and it's my turn to get with the program.

They wrap Zoe in a blanket so tight that she looks like a burrito. In her hands, pressed up against her chest is Sparkle. She reveals why she's named such when the large overhead lamp is positioned above Zoe's head. Pink wings perversely glitter.

"Now, Zoe, I'm going to give you a little shot so you won't feel anything bad. This is going to sting a little, honey."

I stare at the needle, which looks gigantic as it comes toward her chin. Zoe sees it too and she begins crying. Her lips are quivering.

"It's okay, baby," I tell her, wondering how much of that is a bald-faced lie.

The needle stabs into her skin and she cries. I wonder how numb she's actually going to be during this. I tighten my grip on her. My arms are like a brace. I never stop talking to her.

"It's going to be okay, Zoe. It'll all be over soon. I promise. Daddy's right here. I'm not going anywhere, baby. You're going to be alright." They're just words. I don't know what they mean.

Then comes the needle and the suture. Her eyes are wide with terror as she sees the first needle was just the beginning of this horrible procedure. She starts to cry, but bless her heart, she's really trying to be brave and tamp down the tears. It's not working all that well, but she's trying. Beads of sweat begin to appear on her forehead and within seconds she's soaking wet as the doctor stabs the needle in one side of the gash, then sews into the other. Again. And again. And again.

"You're doing great, Zoe. You're doing great. I love you. I'm right here," I tell her. Then I look at the doctor, unable to hide my anger at him for simply doing his job. Too slowly, if you ask me. "How much longer, doctor?"

"Almost done, Zoe," he tells us. Zoe whimpers and the sounds she's making are breaking my heart. I can't believe I'm ringside for this. I can't believe this happened on my watch. This is my little girl being worked over like a patchwork quilt. Blood is everywhere. I'm sweating now. But still I hold her tight, tight, tight as I can. We're practically motionless.

Finally the doctor is finished, and when he is, I release my stranglehold on Zoe and she bursts into tears. The sobs are all-consuming, and as the blanket is relaxed from around her body, she keeps a tight grasp on Sparkle, holding it as close to her chest as she possibly can. Her body is drenched in sweat. As is mine.

After much rocking and much cooing and speaking softly to her, rubbing her hair, she's quiet, exhausted. There are no more tears to cry. She realizes it's over now and she's just this weak, helpless thing.

I thank the doctor and the nurse and carry Zoe in my arms out into the waiting room where David sits with Sam. Both shoot up from their chairs when they see us.

"Zoe, are you alright?" David asks her gently.

"Yes." The reply is barely audible.

"What did they do to you, Zoe?" Sam wants to know.

"We'll talk about that later, Sam," I say. "Right now you two need to sit with Zoe while I fill out some paperwork. I'll be back as fast as I can. David, can you…?" And his arms outstretch for the gentle handoff.

As I walk toward the hospital administration desk to sort out the ER bill, I am racked with guilt for allowing this to happen. It swallows me up whole, and I feel like a failure as a father. We should have taped that rug down. I shouldn't have put her on the bed; it was too high for her. The condemnations wear on. She'll have a scar. This thought makes me wonder what kind of psychological scars she'll have. I know I'll have them.

After getting through all the paperwork, I return to the waiting room, and to my surprise, I find all three in good spirits. David is explaining how the stitches coming out don't hurt at all, especially compared to them going in, and Zoe seems to be absorbing this with heart. Sam keeps angling his head to look at her sutured chin. I see the unicorn in Zoe's hands.

"Zoe, is Sparkle okay?"

"She's better now."

"Well, she was a champ for being there with you," I say and then reach out and stroke the fuzzy unicorn's head.

In the lights of the hospital, she sparkles a little. I know Zoe's will come back to her eventually.

* * *

"So, what did you think?"

"Weak," says my son. "The reboot just isn't as good as the first round. The cast is kinda lame and Jennifer Lawrence makes a lousy Mystique."

We are much older now and, apparently, scathing *X-men* critics.

"Oh, I like her," I tell him.

"She sucks," Sam insists.

"Did Zoe see it?"

"I'm pretty sure she didn't like it either."

"It looked cheap and it lacked soul. The relationships just weren't as rich as the first ones that Singer directed, the ones we saw when you guys were little. Will you see the next one?"

Then my son joins legions of little shits who are the bane of every studio's existence.

"I may watch a bootleg of it online."

This launches me into a tirade about piracy, but he doesn't listen to me. Those years, for both him and his sister, are long gone.

* * *

It is decades later now and I am packing up their toys. This will be my third home since the house with the pool. Along with the new house is a new boyfriend, though we don't live together. I've found out I'm really lousy at playing house. So I live, happily, on my own. I don't see the kids any more every other weekend. They have their own lives now. Instead of playing with superheroes, now they're the ones in capes. My son is a hotshot with an energy company, soaring up the corporate ladder. My daughter is a social worker, swooping in and saving little lives.

I look in the cardboard box and take a sad inventory of who's made it this far alive. There are only a few remaining X-men, one or two missing an arm or a leg here and there. Due to lack of space, the Kaleidoscope Doll House has been lost, though I kept all the furniture. There are a couple of stuffed animals. No Sparkle though. The haul is pretty light. Almost all of the X-men have been lost to time or disappeared during a visit back to the kids' house, promises of bringing them back never kept. You lose so many things as you grow older.

If you think I had it all so easy because I was only a dad on Tuesdays and every other weekend, I should tell you I was not spared from having to discipline them or say the word "no," just as I wasn't spared being up close and personal for Zoe's first—and, thankfully, only—ER visit. Nor did I escape the singular agony of watching my son experience his first heartbreak. But these episodes were few, and as soon as they come to mind, I scurry them away and replace them with happier memories. How every adventure was big and every smile utterly genuine.

When we played, the play became everything. I'd never thrown myself into something with the same wild abandon as I did when I was with those two kids. Never soared higher than when I was lifting them off the ground. Never was as in-the-moment as I was when I was down on their level, seeing them fully, eye-to-eye. And because I was once a child, I know they will never be quite as engaged as they were then.

This box won't be opened until my daughter has kids. My son has sworn he will never have them, a vow I can't help but take as a slight critique on the whole state, if not my handling of it. But I hope they both get to experience this, to know this feeling. They've seen it from one perspective, but they should see it, too, from the other side. I wish they could see the other side of this, see their own kids as we were.

We were fantastic.

We were wonderful.

We were marvelous.

STEP & REPEAT

The Shrinking Violet

Part One: Step

Every year *Out* magazine publishes its Hot 100 List. *Out* is like *People*, *Entertainment Weekly*, *Forbes*, *Rolling Stone*, *Vogue*, *Sports Illustrated*, *Esquire*, and *Dwell* all rolled into one, only for gay people. The "Out 100" is a roster honoring the 100 movers and shakers, the innovators and imagineers—i.e., the cool kids—who held particular sway over politics, entertainment, business, science, sports, the arts, and philanthropy that year. Somehow, my work as a writer, director, and producer of English-language anime has landed me on this list.

This much of me is flattered and *THIS* much of me is really uncomfortable with the honor. That discomfort increases exponentially the closer it comes for the publication to hit the stands. It seems like every day there's a new development about this thing that I never asked to receive but nevertheless got. It's not like I filled out a form or application to get this. I guess somebody said something. Don't get me wrong, I'm not ungrateful, but I cave under attention. *Nothing to see here, people. Just a guy tryin' to make a living and not kill or maim anyone doing it. Move on. No pictures, please.*

"Do you have a headshot?" asks Chris, the company PR man. I'm assuming he's the reason all this is happening. I should be grateful to him but the closer it gets to D-Day, the more it looks like blame.

"Why would *I* have a headshot?" I ask, withering. Actors have headshots. Directors don't. So there was no point in taking me to a Glamour Shots in some suburban mall. Though I'd probably benefit from that whole soft-focus thing.

"*Out* wants a picture," he tells me. "Can ya get one?"

My stomach drops.

"Yeah, I can get one."

"By Monday?"

"Sure," I say shakily.

"Thanks."

And with that, he's walking back to his office and I'm running through a list in my mind of photographers who owe me favors. I've hired a few lensmen for publicity shoots. Maybe they can do me a solid and snap a pic of me where I don't look terrible. I call a guy I've worked with several times, John Conroy. He's so handsome he should be in front of the camera, not behind it. Which is exactly what he once did. But very early in his modeling career he realized he wasn't going to be the pretty boy forever and he better segue to a career with even better legs than his. Now he's got a dashing touch of gray on the temples and he's busier than ever—on both sides of the camera. And he's just as talented in either place. Now I see him golfing, driving a luxury car, getting onto a private plane, etc. on the pages of almost every magazine I pick up. But I'm wanting him back on the other side of the camera so I call him to make sure he's available. I figure he's always made my actors look dead-sexy; maybe he can make me look at least presentable, perhaps even printable.

After a rambling phone call peppered with *I'm sorry to ask this buts* and *You can of course say no if you can't do its*, he graciously offers to snap the shot on Sunday. I show up at his studio early Sunday morning with a change of clothes (as ordered) and the whole ordeal is only mildly tortuous. Maybe if I was gorgeous I'd have a better time with it, but I just feel like a tool posing. But John is great and I thank him and leave his studio with a disc filled with images. When I get home, after about two hours and twice as many martinis, I select two to send to the magazine. One is of me semi-scowling, the other of me gesturing while talking. The best thing I can say about the photographs is I don't hate them. But to John's credit, my painfully non-photogenic mug looks presentable enough to send to a fancy glossy national magazine. I hand the disc to Chris on Monday morning so he can send it to the magazine and the last hurdle is leapt. Now comes the nail biting until the issue comes out.

A couple weeks later, I'm in my neighborhood Barnes & Noble, and as I'm perusing the magazine rack, I see an *Out* magazine with the words *The 100 men and women who rocked 2006* in big red-and-black type on the cover. I had forgotten that even though it's the December issue, it streets much earlier than that. This throws me off my axis like a physical shove, and I break into a cold sweat. Shaky hands take the magazine down from the row of others.

There on the cover, smiling back at me—or giving me their best pouty looks—are singer Rufus Wainwright, actress Anne Hathaway, supermodel and philanthropist Iman, director John Cameron Mitchell, and fashion designer Michael Kors.

Holy shit! I made a list with *these* people? WTF? The magazine has two big wet palm prints where my sweaty hands are clutching it.

My fingers flip through to the center of the magazine, estimating where the cover feature begins. I freeze when I see the spread. Glowing across two pages are giant blue neon letters spelling OUT

100. I turn the page and start reading the article. To my surprise, I don't madly tear through pages until I find my name. Instead, I sit down right there on the floor and begin reading the entire article. I'll see it just like everyone else will see it. After all, no one else is going to be searching through for my name like an addict looking for crack. I won't either.

Suddenly, I have a terrible thought. This is a pretty impressive list of people. Maybe they decided I didn't make the cut after all! That this isn't the Hot 100, it's the Hot 99. *Shut up, idiot, and read. The cover* said *100.*

The tributes are really nice. They're beautifully, succinctly written with journalistic flair and a minimum of fawning. They don't gush, they simply list the person's accomplishments and maybe occasionally translate into why this constitutes "hot." Aside from the stars on the cover, the list includes people like book cover designer Chip Kidd. *Running With Scissors* author Augusten Burroughs. Gore *fucking* Vidal. Fashion designer of the moment, Zac Posen. Fitness Nazi Jackie Warner. *Will & Grace* co-creator Max Mutchnick. Filmmaker Pedro Almodovar. Scissor Sisters Jake Shears and Babydaddy.

Then I get to page 120.

There my name is. And…

It's spelled wrong.

Once again, the dreaded "ph" versus "v" debate must have occurred and, as usual, "ph" won. In *Out*'s defense, I get asked this question all the time. And I wouldn't have put it past my own PR guy to have misspelled my name before *Out* did. Because I go by Steven and not "Steve" everyone always (wrongly) assumes it's with a "ph."

But we don't have to worry about that now, do we, Ste7en? *No, we don't, Ste7en.*

But here's the Big Picture gripe I have about the typo: if I had been acting like an egomaniacal asshole about this deal, I'd understand the need for God to humble me a little. If I was going around shoving copies of the magazine in everyone's hand telling them that I was so hot a magazine had to write about me, that would be one thing. But I told *maybe* four people. No one in my family even knows. I haven't come close to going full-on diva or anything. So why is the cosmos using this as a humility lesson?

I still don't know, but to my credit, I find it hilarious. After a *Well, whadya know* headshake, I begin to read what they wrote.

"A star producer" is how the paragraph starts. Now that's pretty flattering. This may not be as painful as I feared. As I read along I can start to see why, yeah, they might have chosen me.

The magazine mentions that I was named Producer of The Year by *Play* magazine, an award that had previously not been awarded and hasn't been awarded since. They name-drop my most ambitious project up to that time, *The Super Milk-Chan Show* which aired on Cartoon Network. (I recorded an Americanized adaptation of the show, replacing all the Japanese humor with jokes Westerners would understand. Out of respect for the source material, I also recorded a version that was a version that was straight off the translation. One rocked, the other sucked. Cartoon Network, naturally, wanted the sucky version and the show aired to massive disdain with fan outcry demanding to know why they didn't use the "fosterized" version. When will people learn to *listen* to me?) They also note that in one year I had written and directed both *Gilgamesh* and *Ghost Stories*. And you couldn't get two shows more different from each other than those two.

The *Out* piece is a fantastic write-up that fits nicely alongside my page-mates, choreographer Kenny Ortega, theatre auteur Robert Wilson, future *American Horror Story* muse Sarah Paulson, and others.

I finish reading the article, reread my blurb one more time, then promptly grab five copies of the magazine and go to the cash register, resisting the temptation to shove it into the poor Barnes &

Noble employee's hand and beg they turn to page 120 and confirm I hadn't just imagined the whole thing.

The only disappointment—even greater than the typo—is that my picture isn't there. And it's not so much that mine isn't there but whose picture is. Right in the center of the page and very close to my name is a large photograph of an overweight man-child with a cherubic face and an upraised fist. He's some Australian comedian and I'm sure he's a very delightful person but I just can't believe that his pic was that much better than mine. He's shot wearing a too-tight little denim shirt, Daisy Dukes, and cowboy boots. Am I such an eyesore that this guy beat me? It is more than a little depressing.

In an interesting side note, that was the last year *Out* magazine didn't shoot the entire list themselves. From 2007 on, the magazine would take portraits of every single subject, all 100. The conclusion is obvious: my picture was singlehandedly so damn terrible that I caused them to revise their entire editorial policy for the Hot 100 issue and they upped the photography budget substantially.

So all you winners after 2006, you're welcome.

Part Two: Repeat

Within a day or so of getting the magazine, I receive something in the mail from *Out*, a medium-size bubble envelope. I open it, fully thinking they've simply returned the disc of headshots Chris sent. Instead there's an index-card-sized piece of acrylic plastic, black with knocked-out letters that read clear. Also in the packet is a black acrylic key. The card reads:

> YOU AND A GUEST ARE CORDIALLY INVITED TO CELEBRATE THE MEN AND WOMEN WHO HAVE HELPED SHAPE GAY CULTURE THIS YEAR. Join us as we present awards for Artist of the Year, Humanitarian of the

> Year, Stylemaker of the Year, Entertainer of the Year, and Ingenue of the Year. You must bring the attached key for admittance. Key admits you and one guest and is nontransferable. Please RSVP to Out100RSVP@out.com. Attendees must be at least 21. Dress is chic. Produced by BMF Media Group.

Now what should be a happy moment, wherein I am overjoyed I'm being asked to a hip party given in my honor, quickly turns into a tide of panic. All the negatives of the situation arise like a hydra, each head hissing at me with their individual reasons: *What the hell are you going to do there? Hang out with the Artist, Humanitarian, Stylemaker, Entertainer, and Ingenue of the Year and trade notes? What on earth would you possibly have to contribute to a conversation between Rufus Wainwright and John Cameron Mitchell other than, "I saw you on your first tour at a dive bar." and "I'm sorry, but I never saw* Hedwig.*"? You're too old to be comparing ingenue notes with Anne Hathaway. And what would you possibly wear that wouldn't make both Iman and Michael Kors wonder what riffraff this party let in here anyway? Furthermore*, says the last nasty head, *the event is in less than two weeks. It's a pity invite.*

I open this in the studio, so right away the engineer by my side and the actor in the booth are let in on my good fortune-slash-dilemma and I am immediately chastised for even thinking of skipping the thing. They're right of course. Even crippling anxiety won't be a good enough excuse to let me off the hook, not even to me. But I'm still terrified by just the thought of this thing. It's ridiculous, I know, but it's a fear I cannot tame. I can hang with an interviewer. I can chat with a reporter. I can give a talk to several hundred people in a large banquet room of a hotel or convention center. But that's not *me. Now* Me is going to have to navigate a sea of people far cooler, hipper, and lovelier—and that makes me break out in a cold, unattractive sweat. I realize that I can, of course, shop for something "chic" to wear as commanded. But me and a guest? Who in the world would I take to something like…

That's when it hit me. That is the key. The plus one.

I know just who to call.

New York

The cab comes to a stop on the corner. I roll the window down and the glass is replaced by something that reflects the colors and the light even more beautifully. The Something leans forward.

"Sorry I'm late," she tells me. "I was on the phone with Mr. Box Office."

The Something is Taylor Hannah. And, boy, is she something. I met Taylor at an open casting call for *The Super Milk-Chan Show.* Besides the animation, the show has some live-action footage, and to replace that, I'd come up with a sitcom-like series of skits that intersperses with the admittedly boring anime. It's a ploy to keep the viewer watching and it worked. I had jumped behind the camera previously on a show called *Colorful!*, making a faux documentary about the show and the cast. (Think *Best in Show* with anime voice actors.) The fans ate it up so it gave me the courage and drive to push that idea further and *Super Milk Chan* gave me the perfect opportunity. The show featured a crackerjack cast who were all game to play exaggerated versions of themselves for a laugh. But along with the usual actors, I wanted to introduce someone new, a bombshell to drive the men wild and turn the women a slight shade of green.

I called the hottest modeling agency in town and asked them to send me a half dozen ringers. Taylor was the first person I saw and I knew instantly I didn't need to see any others. I'll never forget the moment I laid eyes on her.

She walked into the studio lobby, all five feet ten inches of her. Legs for days, long brunette hair, eyes the color of summer grass, and a high-wattage smile that looked like her orthodontist must have been the best Jewish dentist in the universe and by Jewish dentist I mean God. She wore a simple blouse and slightly faded jeans and at the end of her long denim gams were stiletto suede floral boots.

You know those people that just have It? That unmistakable *something* that differentiates them from the rest? It's like they have some extra quality the rest of us didn't get but can pick up on. We can notice it, but we can't name it. It's something rapturous but something we can't put our finger on but we know it when we see it. Taylor Hannah was the first person I had ever met who had It. And it was obvious just watching her walk into the studio lobby.

She had done a little acting before so she wasn't alien to it and she was excited about performing the voiceovers for a panoply of characters and game for the live-action shoot. She was a growing talent, and she knew how to take direction well. I fell for her immediately.

Then she told me how old she was.

Everyone pegs Taylor at twentysomething. Whether it's her height or her adult beauty, it would be nothing for any man to hit on her. Then, when they find out (as they inevitably do) that she's *fifteen years old*, they all feel like pedophiles. I'm gay and have no sexual attraction to her at all and *I* still felt like one. But the role was nothing more than an ingenue femme fatale; it wasn't like there was any nudity or anything untoward about it. There was some pretty harsh language in the anime script—none of it hers—and when I talked to Taylor's mother about it, she said if Taylor didn't care, she didn't either. Taylor said she didn't and I gleefully cast her in the part.

While working together, we become friends and see each other socially outside the studio. Taylor is splitting her time between

Houston and New York, and at this stage in her career she is pretty much in New York full time. She is the only person I know in the city, so when the invitation from *Out* magazine came, I thought of her. One, she is a blast to be around. She is a sweet and lively conversationalist. The bonus is that she is Hollywood-hot and if she is with me, all the attention will be on her and take the spotlight off me. Just because this is "my night" doesn't mean I'm comfortable with it. It is my plan to go to this thing, lay low, have a drink, maybe see a famous person or two, and then get out with my dignity intact.

She is already proving to be the best choice for a date by dropping this bombshell about Mr. Box Office. I shove open the cab's door, move over, and she slides in beside me, her long legs visible through the slit in the gown-length dress she wears, a cabernet-colored confection that hugs her like a glove. It is sleeveless and has a choker neckline. Her hair falls delicately around her bare shoulders and she looks, as usual, like a million bucks. I, by extension, appear to be worth at *least* $39.95. I wear black slacks and shoes and a pale lavender shirt. Over the shirt is a jacket I'd found and splurged on, a perfectly fitted off-the-rack designer number, black with pinstripes and a lavender and sky-blue floral pattern over the left breast where a pocket should have been. It sounds faggy as hell but it looks pretty cool. I don't know if I am exactly pulling off "chic" like the invitation demanded, but it's the best I could come up with without hiring a fucking stylist.

Mr. Box Office isn't his real name, of course. But this very bankable marquee movie star had a healthy run of action flicks in the 90s, a key part in one of the seminal independent movies of the 90s, and the requisite Hollywood marriage to another actor of equal fame. That union had dissolved quite publicly and his ex-wife has now taken up with a young man about twenty years their junior while he remains unattached.

But it seems like Mr. Box Office isn't quite happy with that arrangement. That's where Taylor comes in.

It was just the other night, Halloween, and she and some girlfriends were going to go out. They had landed on a pretty great costume gimmick. Each found a vinyl dress in a color—red, purple, yellow, and orange—and they went as the Fanta girls. Taylor was Orange.

They're going out clubbing, and of course, despite being underage, the bouncer lets them in one of the hottest clubs in New York City because they're gorgeous. So the girls are dancing and having a great time on the floor when all of a sudden one of the club's employees comes over and taps Taylor on the shoulder.

"Mr. Box Office wants to meet you," he tells her. Like this is a big deal she should appreciate.

"Who?"

"Mr. Box Office."

"Oh," she says. And keeps dancing. "Okay."

The man leaves her only to return a song later.

"He *really* wants to meet you."

Taylor *harrumphs* and tells the guy she'll go meet him.

The man leads her to a VIP table and, sure enough, there's Mr. Box Office looking charming and handsome and, well, box office-y. He chats her up. Asks her about herself. Liking what he hears, he asks her out. Taylor is friendly but is, to be honest, more interested in getting back to the dance floor with her girlfriends. Mr. Box Office persists. Won't she go out with him? She's a little buzzed from the drink, and a little frustrated she's not dancing anymore so she figures she'll just cut to the chase and end this right now.

"Do you know how old I am?"

"No."

"I'm sixteen."

Meanwhile, in the cab, I'm freaking out.

"I can't believe you just slammed him with that."

"Just wait," she says. She then morphs her body into the posture of a cruisy, boozy player. She hunches her shoulders. "He just shrugs and goes, *Okay.*"

We both burst out laughing. Then I find out she met him once—no hanky panky, get your mind out of the gutter—and that little rendezvous went so well he wanted to see her again. Only this next "date" would be in St. Tropez. Turns out the trip was already planned and he had the yacht booked so…

"What did you tell him?" I ask.

"I told him I needed to ask my mother," she says.

See? Beautiful *and* funny.

* * *

Our cab pulls up to the venue and it's one of the swankier event spaces in New York, The Capitale. I had done zero research on this place. I never googled it or anything like that. So I am a little taken aback at the scale of the event. Giant searchlights are parked in front of the building, making everything look even more intimidating than I imagined it would be. I'm glad I have Taylor with me. She's something for the spotlights to shine on.

As we pass inside, there's someone there to take our precious plexiglass key, our entree into the party. They're standing right before a long Step and Repeat. A Step and Repeat is what you call that logo-emblazoned backdrop that celebrities pose in front of on their way down the red carpet. It looks like a gauntlet of horror to me. A nice attendant takes our key and tries to usher us toward the red carpet and the phalanx of photographers there snapping pictures. I quickly beg off and grab Taylor by the arm and we duck aside. I maneuver us near a round table just away from the media melee. I notice the table is covered with loose flower blossoms and a few rows of small cards but in the flash of the cameras and the chaos near the carpet I don't look any closer.

"What's the matter?" Taylor asks.

"I don't want to go down that thing," I say.

"Oh come on, it'll be fun."

"No, I really don't want to."

"Steven."

"I really don't want to go."

"Okay," she replies, no trace of disappointment in her voice. She seems so casually at ease with everything and everything is turning me practically feral.

"Let's get a drink," I say, sounding more like begging.

The interior of the Capitale, away from the strobing cameras, is drenched in violet and pink lights and it's jam-packed. Guests mill about, grabbing drinks at one of the many station bars, each anchored by a giant ice sculpture and manned by a hunky bartender pushing Absolut grapefruit cocktails. There are large video projection screens with spotlit letters reading THE OUT 100. Everyone's definitely in compliance with the invite request. Chic is the word of the night.

I don't know what's wrong with me. I spent a small fortune on this stupid jacket I'm wearing; I should at least feel like I look the part.

We get a couple of drinks from the bar and check the place out. I can't see a sign of Iman or any of the other ninety-eight "hot listers" around anywhere. I assume not many of them could make the swank proceedings. If they are here, I doubt they're just cowering and trying to sink into the wallpaper like I am.

Eventually the ceremony starts where they award the five special honors. A video begins playing with all the honorees, a montage of beautiful portraits and/or names of the list-makers in a tasteful, elegant font that blooms onto the screen before fading away for the next honoree. I stare at the video, glad for something for me to focus on. Faces and names I recognize and some I don't float by on a black sea, and right after a lovely photograph of Martina

Navratilova drifts out of frame, a name appears that I more than recognize. It's my name, coming right after Navratilova's. I can't believe it.

It's spelled correctly.

I don't know how but someone figured out how to spell my name, and while it's still wrong in the magazine itself, there it is, *Steven Foster* on the screen. Taylor whoops and since she has a drink in her hand and can't clap, she puts her fingers to her lips and does that whistle thing that everybody else but me seems to be able to do. She then gives me a huge, tight hug with her girlie-but-Amazonian-model arms. She's gushing complimentary things but everything is a blur for me, everything sped up and slowed down somehow at the same time. The lights, the noise, the screen, it's all just a whirling chaos.

The video finishes and then someone's talking but I can't tell what they're saying.

"Are you ready to go?" I ask.

"Are you *serious*?" Taylor is shocked.

"Well, maybe after one more drink," I reluctantly hedge.

Within sips of our second drink, I suggest our leaving again and while Taylor eyes the dance floor with a slightly wistful glance, she's pretty much "whatever you say" about the whole thing. I feel like I'm disappointing her. I can't help it though. All I want to do is disappear.

As we're leaving the venue, I once again notice the table by the entrance with the flowers. The rows of cards have diminished, leaving only a few on the table. They're name tags. I ask someone standing close by what they're for.

"What are these?"

"Nametags for the 100 honorees," the aide tells me.

Taylor steps in.

"He's one of them!"

"Oh," says the aide, surprised. "What's your name?"

"Steven Foster."

The aide fishes the nametag from the table.

"Oh no. You were supposed to get this when you first came in and walked the carpet. Then you would have gone to the VIP area."

My heart sinks.

"VIP area?"

"It's a separate area just for the 100 honorees and their guests," he says, looking almost as disappointed as I am. "Kelis was playing."

So Kelis was bringing my milkshake to the yard. And I was in the stupid house. I can't believe it.

Taylor sees my disappointment but chooses to take the bright side. "Come on, let's go," she suggests smiling, pulling my arm toward this mysterious VIP area.

But it's so late in the game now, I feel there's almost no point. I beg off and we leave the venue.

We stand there, waiting for a cab. There are a few people leaving the event, a few others standing there smoking, looking glamorous. The giant spotlights shoot two huge white beams into the night sky. Taylor turns to me.

"Did you have a good time?"

"Did *you* have a good time? I feel bad I fucked up and we didn't go down the carpet and that stupid Step and Repeat wall. We didn't get to hang out with the celebrity contingent."

"I had a blast."

"Really?" I find this less than believable. Taylor gets stalked by Hollywood celebrities. She would have fit right in with the in-crowd.

"Oh my god," she says. She's beaming. She means it. "It was worth the whole evening just watching your face. When you saw your name onscreen, you looked so happy. I just watched you. It was really something to see. You looked *so* happy, Steven."

So here it is: proof that, for at least a couple of seconds, I enjoyed it. Where all the paranoia and insecurity had left me alone and I was happy. Where, somehow, I was able to just be in the moment and be a little proud of myself, if only for a fast, fleeting moment.

Too bad I missed the rest of the evening.

LILY

The Protector

So this just happened. And I'll never have to question my bravery—or is that stupidity?—ever again.

I'm dog sitting for my son. She's a sweet little thing, my grand-dog-ter. She's a mutt with an Australian/cocker-spaniel lineage from what I've been told, only she's a hair taller than a cocker and much more spry. In fact, I would suspect she's a cocaine user if she had fingers instead of paws, and I've yet to see a straw anywhere. So I'm thinking this just must be her natural state. She is always at a Level Nine on the excite-o-meter. So much so that she is able to get herself completely airborne, almost three feet off the ground. It's a little remarkable. She looks as if a small explosive charge went off under her as she and her fur fly into the air at any *boom!* moment. She usually does this repeatedly when there is a treat involved, or a leash is picked up. So I walk her a lot. I like to see flying dogs.

I live on a circle. If my house is at the 12, I'm around the 7 to 8 part of the round little lane when Lily (that's the dog) and I are just walking along minding our own business. Then, all of a sudden, this HUGE barking sound comes roaring up and a giant copper-

and-gray pit bull charges out from under the dark canopy of this tree looming large in someone's yard, its giant branches forming such a deep patch of shade that I never see the monster coming. Now all this happens in just a few seconds:

Lily charges right back at the dog, which is about nine times her size. I yell at her, "Lily!" but the leash continues to unspool the farther she gets from me.

Pit bull's coming.

Lily sees the pit bull very clearly now, immediately changes her mind about attacking him, and high-tails it down the street, the leash slack letting her get several yards from me before I snap to what's going on and jerk the leash, for some reason thinking she's going to be better off with me protecting her than a pit bull gaining on her as she tries to escape.

She immediately takes the hint when the collar snaps her back and she turns and runs toward me and the oncoming pit bull. (She's barking now and has been, this whole time. Bull, too. His is just lower and larger sounding and hers sounds kind of like Owen Meany.)

She comes toward me and I sling her behind me with the leash, the pit bull still charging. Then, this happens:

I lean FORWARD and OVER, bending so that I BARE MY FACE at the pit bull's level so now we can see each other, eye to eye. On hindsight, this seems not such a great idea.

But this is not hindsight, this is happening now. It's ALL happening now.

Then, as I'm bent over, something large and deep from within my chest or lungs or somewhere begins to explode out of my throat and my mouth is screaming, screaming right in the pit bull's charging mouth and angry eyes.

I yell, in a voice that sounds as though it belongs to some satanic demon instead of some mild-mannered dog walker.

"GET AWAY! Get the FUCK away!"

And…

The pit bull stops. Quickly he shuffles backward, turns around to get further back, then spins around back at me, almost as if he's realized who's the bigger force here.

But whatever it was, it's over. My loud, demonic shriek echoes up the circle toward the twelve, and Lily and I are walking away—quickly, but we're walking away. And she pipes up.

"Yip! Yip!"

I tell her, "Shut up and keep walking."

She obeys.

I see my next-door neighbor, who must have heard my hell yell, as he comes jogging down the circle, swinging a blue aluminum baseball bat. At the same time, this muscled guy from out of nowhere wheels up on his bike. I don't know if they're there to take care of the pit bull or attack whatever thing made that horrible scream. The pit bull, meanwhile, is still listening to my advice to "get the FUCK away."

That's when I find out from the two men that this is one of two pit bulls this cranky older man on our circle has. The other one is supposedly meaner. The muscle guy introduces himself to me and tells me that one of the bulls chased him on his bike a month ago. My next-door neighbor is still swinging the bat, sneering and looking like he's been wanting to do this for years.

"I'm just looking for an excuse to swing at those dogs. Just one," he tells me, a little too much bloodlust in his eyes.

The pit bull is loping around his yard and the neighbor's yard, looking my way but keeping his distance when Lily, now fearless once again, yells at the pit bull herself. She does not use profanity, but still, I tell her to zip it.

There's a kindly war veteran who lives at the 10 on the circle, and my neighbor and the muscle guy walk with me until we get to his house. That's when they beg off and say they're going to visit the old man, who's sitting in his garage on a recliner—as he always does at this time in the afternoon—and join him for a beer. I say goodbye, thank my knights, and Lily and I continue walking back up the circle to my house and it hits me.

Did I just stare down a pit bull?

Yes. I did. It might not have been the smartest move in the world, but it worked. And I feel pretty damn good about myself right now. Standing up a little taller, my eyes sharp and focused and darting around for other dangers.

But there are none. Lily's forgotten about the pit bull and is eagerly leaping toward the backyard where she has seen squirrels. Lily loves to do to the squirrels what the pit bull did to us. They don't yell back at her. They just run.

Me? I don't run.

I stand my ground.

BECOSPLAY

The Sheep in Wolf's Clothing

I HONESTLY DON'T KNOW HOW I GOT MYSELF INTO THIS ONE, BUT I am throwing a wedding shower. I'm not doing it alone. I have a partner. We both have known the bride-to-be through work, though we each intersect her from two very different occupations. Stephanie, the bride-to-be, teaches drama at a school for the performing arts where my co-host is a math teacher. To be a math teacher at a school dedicated to the arts is like being broccoli at a candy buffet. I feel for the woman.

The hall where I pass Stephanie isn't in a school but rather the studio where I work in the entertainment ghetto of Japanese anime. Stephanie is a voice actor I occasionally cast in shows I'm producing.

When I tell people I work in anime and explain that I work with voice actors all day, someone invariably tells me how "people at the office" are really charmed by "all the funny voices I do." Then I'm subjected to an impromptu audition where I am given a rendition of how Karen in Accounting sounds and always—*always*—an impression of Stewie from *Family Guy*. Everyone thinks they are so gifted they can do Stewie, but the fact of the matter is most people can do Stewie. Everyone also thinks being a voice actor is somehow all voice part and no act part, no training required. Let's just get this on the record for all you wannabe voice actors out there: it's not what you think it is.

Most everybody believes voiceover is the easiest gig in the world when, in actuality, it's one of the hardest. All your go-to's and reliables, your bag of tricks, are gone. You're limited to just your voice. Everything—every emotion, action, and nuance of characterization—has to come through the voice alone. If you're recording ADR like you are in anime, you also have to get the mouth movements right because you're replacing Japanese lines with English ones. It's artistry meets technical prowess.

The best voice actor, for ADR producers and directors anyway, is someone who is (1) an actual actor, as well as someone who (2) possesses such a dexterous voice, they're able to switch genders believably or play a certain age one minute, ageless the next. Not all actors have such range but when you find one that does, you do whatever you can to hold onto them. Anime features a disproportionate number of thirteen-year-old heroes at the center of the story so youthful-sounding actors are always a find. Stephanie Wittels is one of those actors with that kind of voice. She could be any age girl or woman. She can even be a teenager or little boy. She's chameleonic.

It's a voice I was introduced to, full gale force one day, between studio sessions. Another director was in the lobby as I was saying goodbye to the actress from my recording session. After seeing her to the parking lot, I went back inside the lobby and the other director makes *really* hasty introductions—"Steven, this is Stephanie Wittels, Stephanie, Steven"—before bolting down the hall down to studio row.

Immediately, this tiny person pops up in front of me. Sorta like a live action whack-a-mole.

"Why don't you talk to me?" she demands to know.

My head does one of those *aya-aya-aya* blurry headshakes. But it's more Looney Toons than *Jacob's Ladder* because, though her tone is threatening, when I look down at her, she can't keep a straight face to make the threat remotely believable. Still, give the girl points for committing to the part.

"I've seen you. And you go back *there* with everybody else," she says, one arm pinwheeling behind her, pointing toward the hall. "And you always go down there laughing. And then I see you *come out* laughing."

"No, I don't."

"YES. You do," she assures me.

"Not everybody."

"*Everybody*. And I wanna know why." She's got her hands on her hips now. Never a good sign. But she looks funny doing it. "Because I'm *fun*. I'm *funny*! People *love* me. *You'd* love me. But do I get the chance to be loved by you? No." She sees I'm about to interject. She charges on. "NO! I don't. So I just want you to give me a chance. Because I wanna play with the cool kids too. Because…because I *am* a cool kid. You don't understand. *I* should be with you. I should be with you *all the time*!"

I look down at this little mole-sized person and realize she's right, she is a lotta fun, and later, after her first audition with me, I wind up casting her in every show I can find that has a part for her.

Until…

Less than a year later when she takes the job teaching and the same conversation happens again. Only this time, I am the little loudmouth begging for a place at the table and she is the aloof idiot having no idea what I'm talking about. Just like a man, she wanted me when I wanted nothing to do with her, but now that she had me, I'm little fish tossed overboard.

It gets so bad that I schedule sessions in the evening (that is, before the company made that the norm) and beg my engineer to work late just so Stephanie could come in and record, oh, crowd noise for an hour, which is basically me now resorting to paying her to come talk to me. This is how Stephanie Wittels is. Once she's got you, you're hooked.

Which is why I would do anything for this woman. Though I don't really know her well enough to throw her a *shower*. But you saw how she was before she met me. So when she asked me to co-host a shower for her, I couldn't say no to the little firecracker. I was terrified to think what she'd do to me if I did. But I had to wonder: were there no other girlfriends around? Did I get asked just because I was the closest fag within reach? It's happened before. Even the studio's done it.

An executive from Sony was coming to check out our facility—which was a dump—and they finally realized they had to make the place look presentable. When they were figuring out what to do, their immediate answer was, "Get Steven to do it." To this day I don't know if they asked me because they knew they could—like in every situation—count on me to get the job done or just because I'm gay. Because, you know, *all* the gays know how to decorate. *Ack*.

But back to Stephanie: I am beginning to think she's asked the wrong homo. I didn't wince at the expenses or blink at the effort it would take to coordinate such an important extravaganza. But this occasion calls for a theme and I can't think of anything. My brain begins running down some vague list of pirates, *Star Wars*, frozen princesses, and pretty little ponies. She's not married yet but apparently my brain has blown off this shower and is starting prep on Stephanie's baby one.

I decide to go straight to the source for inspiration, if not a flat-out directive.

"You better have key lime pie," Stephanie tells me, overwhelming me with a bounty of assistance.

"What the hell does that have to do anything? You want Key Lime Pie to be the theme?"

She laughs.

"If you can theme that, sure."

"Key lime pie is not a theme. I'm gonna call your mother."

"Like that'll help."

I'm practically dialing the phone already as I can hear Stephanie's eyes rolling into the back of her fiancé-focused head, grinding like stones over Jesus' tomb—a strange metaphor since Stephanie's Jewish. Which is precisely why I'll use any excuse to call Stephanie's mother.

Like any good Protestant with a Woody Allen jones, I have this thing for Jewish mothers. Stephanie's mother is the first one I'd ever met, so she's subject to all the stupid mooning of a brony spotting his first unicorn.

In one of those moves that could never work for anyone else—but Stephanie manages to pull it off—she decides to bring along her parents to one of my Sunday Fundays, an invitation-only fete, not because it's oh-so-exclusive but because I have a tiny house. This Sunday-morning church alternative has become slightly legendary and almost as sacred. Sunday Funday is basically just a pot luck brunch. It's in the details where it becomes transcendent. This is the only pot luck I've ever seen where each guest wants to top everybody else so badly that they show up with their own cooking equipment. That goes from carrying a small blowtorch in their pocket to crystallize the sugary lid on the homemade creme brûlées to pulling up in a pickup truck with a vat of peanut oil to deep fry a turkey. Water and coffee are served, but liquids such as these mostly are ignored in favor of the mimosas.

I'm sorry, did I say mimosas? Mimosas are for *pussies*.

Sunday Funday demands mustangs. After three—two if you're one of the thinner, less fermented members of the group—you discover why the drink is given the name of one of the coolest rides ever to roll out of the motor city or a wild, bucking horse. The mustang drink is very much like the car, in that you go from zero to hammered before you're aware you even stepped on the gas, while the effect comes on so strong it feels like a horse kick, the resulting head injury lasting a thrilling, sometimes terrifying eternity. On more than one occasion, a guest has compared the drink to acid. The good shit. From the 60s. The first Sunday Funday began at 10:30 in the morning. It ended at 1:30.

1:30 *a.m.*

It would have gone on longer too if we had at last confirmed a much-rumored vampire lesbian bar someone swore was only a few blocks from my house. But when Stephanie's mother Maureen came, lesbian vampires were instantly passé and I found my new straight crush.

"I don't care if she doesn't know a key lime from a Meyer lemon, I'm calling her," I tell Stephanie.

"Fine. But don't call her now; I just talked to her. She's reading that stupid book. She doesn't answer the phone when she's with The Book."

Like I said, they're Jewish. So naturally I know what she's talking about.

"The *Talmud*?"

"Close. *Fifty Shades of Gray*. Don't get me started."

Christ. Not this thing again.

Look, I have nothing against S&M. I appreciate the hot factor of a good smack on the ass. But ever since this erotic epic of awful prose became A Thing, it has vexed me with an embarrassing combination of curiosity and jealousy made worse only because neither feeling is strong enough to make me (a) read it or (b) write a solid knock-off that could ride its gray Saville Rowe coattails to just a fraction of those millions.

One day an actress, Hilary Haag, comes to the studio to record. In her arms is the blanket she has to have because apparently all recording equipment needs to be kept at the same temperature as a meat locker. The booth is famously icy.

I notice that she might not need the blanket to warm her up because she's got—you guessed it—that book with her. I saw that damn silk tie on the cover and knew exactly what it was.

"Oh God, Hilary, not you too."

"I know," Hilary admits shamelessly. "And it's terrible."

"Then why are you reading it?"

"Because it's terrible."

"Is it hot?"

"Not really. I mean, maybe to a Midwestern house *frau* who's only had vanilla sex with her husband. I bet most fifteen-year-olds think it's totally G-rated."

So during a moment when the engineer is tweaking some of the lines recorded, I ask Hilary to give me a sample of Gen Y's *9 1/2 Weeks.*

Like Stephanie, Hilary can slip into child voice in an instant, which she does, reading the admittedly fairly clunky narrative in that adorable kewpie doll voice of hers. However, when she comes up to the naughtier passages, she lowers her voice and whores it up.

"That's hilarious," I tell her, laughing.

"Right?" Hilary says.

"Now come on. Read me the real thing."

"That was the real thing."

"No, seriously."

"Seriously."

My jaw hits the console. I thought she was kidding, just making up some prose on the spot to be funny.

"No way."

"Yeah," she says with I-told-you-so satisfaction.

"No fucking way."

"I told you so," she says with I-told-you-so satisfaction.

Still, I'm having a hard time wrapping my head around this. I have to confess the raunchy parts are a lot racier than I thought they'd be, but the rest of it? Porn is porn. But bad lit? That's just plain offensive.

They say give 500 monkeys 500 typewriters and eventually one of them will give you *MacBeth*. I wager you give one monkey an open can of alphabet soup and he'll have his own *Fifty Shades of Gray* on Amazon's shelf before you can say "Thank you, Christian, may I have another?"

It's that bad.

Now I find out Stephanie's mom is in the kink-reading club. I'm crushed.

"Don't forget the pie," Stephanie tells me before hanging up.

Argh. Why can't I come up with a goddamn theme for this thing? If I'm going to throw this shower, I want it to be amazing. I need a hook. Why can't I find a hook? And why is everyone reading that stupid, poorly written homage to bondage?

Straight people are fucked up. And *married* straight people are even worse. And soon two more were going to join this horny horde of spanking, choking, dildo-wielding nymphomaniacs.

Stephanie and Michael.

Stephanie.

& Michael.

S. & M.

And, just like that, a theme is born.

* * *

In what may come as a crushing disappointment or unbelievable shock, I do not have a pleasure chest containing a cornucopia of sex toys at my disposal. So while I am relieved—even stoked—that I've come up with a theme, I'm not going to be able to pull it off with things on hand. And this isn't the sorta thing that I'm going to find at Party City.

Let's see, there's Elsa, Dora, Elmo, Anastasia and Christian... Children grow up so fast these days.

I've got a bankrupting, physically endangering, fifty-fifty split of ego and selflessness that drives me to make every single event an Event, whether it's a spur-of-the-moment happy hour or an elaborate photo shoot. I've thrown Halloween parties where there was an actual life-size *Harry Potter* Dementor I made just for the occasion. And I'm no sculptor. (But the statue was *dope*.)

It's not like all the trappings are hard to find, but there is no way I can afford it. I've already laid out a small fortune for the food and the booze and, of course, key lime pies. But if I'm going to have an S&M-themed shower I'll have to buy the entire inventory of the nearest Adam and Eve store. That shit is expensive. Even if I could buy enough props and paraphernalia, what am I gonna do with all the sexual escapade equipment afterward? Will I have to throw a Kentucky Derby party now simply because I have riding crops? You can't return a dildo. What are you going to say? It didn't go with your outfit?

Fortunately, I know this very chic, totally accessible, and more importantly, affordable store for this kind of merchandise. After a quick phone call to ensure they are open late, I hop in my car and speed over. When I arrive, I ring the doorbell. No, it's not that shady. It's also not a store. It's somebody's home.

The front door swings open and standing there is a beautiful older woman, illuminated from the hallway lighting. She is dressed—or undressed rather—in a lacy bra, panties, garter belts, and some other kind of garments held in place by so many straps and snaps I wonder when Victoria's Secret started making skydiving attire.

For the sake of modesty, she is not simply wearing lingerie. She's "covered" by one of those chiffon robes, the cuffs and hem lined with that white material that's like fur from an exploded cat.

This, combined with her ice-blonde hair, makes her look like the lost Gabor sister. I've known Miss Gabor here for decades and in the time I've known her she's successfully morphed from slinky young sex kitten to elegant cougar before my very eyes. Even her nickname is porny.

"Welcome welcome welcome to Blaze Montana's sex paraphernalia warehouse!" she says, motioning her hands like she's one of Drew Carey's sidekicks. That is, if *The Price is Right* product pointers were holding martini glasses, splashing the prizes with moonlit arcs of spilling vodka. "Come in, come in, come in! You'll never believe what I've pulled for you! And don't you like this outfit?! I feel like *Green Acres*!"

That's what I love about Blaze. She's not running to the plastic surgeon to make herself look younger. She's embracing every year she's been given. And she looks terrific for it. I don't think I'm going to handle growing older as well as she does. My whole life I thought that your brain was somehow in some kind of fog that made it so that you didn't mind that your body was breaking down. I thought you just got older and were cool about everything. Now I realize that you have exactly the same mind as you've always had, only now it's trapped in a 1ing cage. Steven Tyler summed it up best: "Inside every old person is a young person wondering what happened."

I see my parents aging before my eyes and they're the same people they've always been. They act like they're still forty; it's just their bodies that don't. There they are, totally aware this is happening, trapped in a front-row seat wearing the most realistic VR glasses yet to be invented. But Blaze resolutely refuses to be put out to pasture, preferring instead to be Zsa Zsa, still sexual and playful, frolicking in evergreen acres.

"Come upstairs!" she beckons, and then I remember her bedroom is something like four flights up. Once I make it to the summit, all I want is to lie down . . . but when I see her bed I realize that's not an option.

The bed has been turned into a glassless showcase featuring every manner of kinkwear and fetish toy. I'm in awe of the staggering variety. And also the remarkable craftsmanship that goes into making something like a two-headed handblown glass dildo.

"I've sterilized everything," she tells me.

"Thanks, but I think I'll stick with the non-insertables."

As I peruse the merchandise, Blaze is more than happy to tell me the story behind each item, and admittedly, some of the stories make me wish I was already old and hard of hearing.

I grab some packing boxes and begin filling them up like an X-rated Santa Claus. I take the booty bounty outside and load it into my car and bid Blaze goodnight.

For the next week or so, I am all about sex. But without the really good part: having it. Doesn't matter. I'm totally into this. I'm going all out with this S&M theme.

The internet, no surprise there, is insanely helpful in finding out everything from medical sexual information to a wealth of pornographic movies and slang. I design a logo for the shower. You want a theme? Oh, I'll show you theme. Using the now-created style guide, I design small cards with sex tips, sex facts, and sex quizzes, my favorite question being which movie title is an actual porno or one I just pulled outta my ass. So to speak.

Butt-man v. Supermom? Not real.

The Fist and The Furious? Take a wild guess.

I'm telling you, I have this shit down. I even have an entrance gag worked up.

But for that I'll need an outfit.

Once again I go to my closet and find it sorely lacking in anything costume-y. Contrary to popular belief, not all gay men have a closet filled with buttless leather chaps. I mean *I* have buttless leather chaps, but I can't wear something like that to a shower. I have to find something appropriate but presentable. Stephanie's mom will be there for God's sake.

So I go to a place called Erotic Cabaret, a shop specializing in negligees, leather, and things like dick-shaped ice cube trays. I go right to their clothing rack and find a section for men. It's a microscopic portion of the store, which makes it all the more miraculous that I actually manage to find something. It's a pair of pants. I don't know what they're made of, some kind of vinyl maybe. They have a strip of this vinyl or whatever running down the outside of each leg, silver rings the size of cock rings interspersed the entire length. I take the pants into the changing room and shimmy into them. They feel amazing. When I look in the mirror, they look pretty good too. I decide to pair them with an NYPD muscle T I have at home, along with some black tape on my biceps, fingerless weightlifting gloves, and a studded dog collar. Then I'll be all set.

Now here's the entrance gimmick: The shower will be held at the math teacher's house, and before the guests are allowed in, they'll have to say, just like at the wedding, if they're here for the groom or the bride. Once they tell me their choice, they'll be allowed in. Then, depending on if they've said Stephanie or Michael…S or M…they'll either have to bend over and get a swat with the riding crop (for M) or I'll give them the paddle and they can whack me on the backside (for S). Then they'll come in and see all the S&M-themed decorations.

When I get to the house, my party partner has done a fantastic job of setting up, so all I have to do is calm down my racing heart, stop sweating, and chill out. It's barely 11 a.m., but I've been up for at least eight hours like a maniac running around at the last minute, so that pitcher of readymade margaritas is looking like a better and better idea all the time. My shower partner has already had one and is reveling in her attire. She sports a black bustier, black mini skirt, black fishnet hose, and black boots. She's the sexiest math teacher I've ever seen. She should wear this to teach the kids the

Pythagorean theorem. They'll pay attention now. She pours me a margarita and I go get dressed.

By the time I am dressed, I'm lightly buzzed and a little frisky. I've got the porn pants on, the wife-beater T-shirt, a thick black armband of satiny electrical tape wrapped around my right bicep, the gloves, the studded dog collar, and most importantly, a paddle at my side and a riding crop in my hand. I look like a Tom-of-Finland sketch come to life. I look at myself in the mirror and I almost don't recognize me. I look pretty sexy. I *feel* sexy.

Thankfully the doorbell rings just before I'm about to become president of my own fan club, and doorknob in one hand, riding crop in the other, I lower my voice to Vin Diesel level.

"S? Or M?" I grunt through the closed door.

Nervous tittering on the other side. I hear someone ask if this is the right house.

"Are you here because you know Michael or Stephanie?' I ask. "Can't let you in till you answer S or M."

"M?" comes the small nervous answer.

I jerk the door open so fast a gust of wind whooshes in. There are three women standing there, a little shocked. I level them with my sexiest stare.

"Who answered the question?"

"She did," two young women point.

"C'mere," I say and grab the woman by the arm, pull her inside the house and slam the door shut.

Inside, I stare at my little coquette.

"Bend over," I command.

Immediately she breaks out into a mischievous smile and obeys. I break character.

"Okay, I'm gonna clap my hands really hard. You make an equivalent reaction sound?" I whisper to her and wink. "Let's make your two friends outside nervous."

"Yes!" she agrees, her eyes wild with conspiratorial excitement. I clap my hands.

Smack!

"Ow!" squeals the woman.

I nod my approval.

"Ooooh," she coos.

"Behave," I tell her. Then I move on to the next guest.

After swatting a plethora of women—and getting a few of my own—the shower commences. Everyone's enjoying the sex quizzes and little notions littered around the house and feeling giddy with the help of the margaritas. It's my first time to a girl's shower, so I'm kind of surprised by the amount of sexy lingerie that's given. I was thinking it was going to be all toasters and bath towels, but instead each box explodes with a new slinky supermodel ensemble in lace. Soon, though, it's time for everyone to leave the presents and go home. Everyone seems really appreciative for a wonderful time.

After giving Stephanie all the leftover key lime pie, I pack up all the stuff I've borrowed from Blaze and take my leave. By the time I get home, it's about 4:30, and I walk into my house in a great mood. Job well done. Now to get out of these clothes.

Not so fast…

It's Saturday and I usually leave the weekends to the new guard. Let the young ones rule the weekend nights. I'll stay in. Besides, it's not like I could go out in public dressed like this. Someone could get hurt!

While I just naturally assumed I'd come home, shuck the sex suit and trade it in for some running shorts and faded concert T, when time comes to change, that's not exactly how things go down.

On my way to the closet, I have to cross the wardrobe and its full-length mirror. What could it hurt to take one last look before I return Steven to normal? So I give myself the once-over.

After about five minutes I notice I'm still standing there staring at myself.

What the hell is the matter with me?

"What's wrong with you?" I ask my reflection. Then I get angry with myself. Truly, really angry. But *why*? Is it because I'm *liking* myself? That can't be it. Can it?

Well fuck that.

I try to shake the feeling but it's quickly replaced by more chastising. *It's Saturday. I should be doing something like tackling that spare room that's a cluttered mess. I should get my taxes ready. I should, I should, I should.* This is the endless soundtrack of my mind. It is the CNN of psyches. Seemed like a great idea at the time, but after seeing there were twenty-four hours of programming to fill, things started getting ugly. It's excruciating. But sometimes, just every so often, I'm able to fire the program director, if only for a short time. So I answer my question, knowing there's only one thing wrong with me.

You don't have any fucking music going, jackass.

My jackbooted feet stomp over to the computer. I load up the Sonos with a house-rattling playlist of Curve, Trent Reznor, Prince, and every other artist that makes aggressively danceable music. Then I proceed to straighten up my sorta cluttered casa but really just use this chore as an excuse to get in some really needed cardio and I *Magic Mike* myself all around the house.

My house is small so I have a generous mirror collection scattered through the place to make it appear bigger. But this time, I feel there aren't nearly enough to see my badass, black-garbed self slinking, sliding, spinning, or pelvic-thrusting by. I can't get over myself. It's a total mystery to me why I'm feeling this way but I am too busy enjoying this self-love fest to analyze it.

Eventually, there's nothing more to pick up off the floor, no counter to clean, and the Sonos switches from Curve's cover of Donna Summer's "I Feel Love" to Terry Gross interviewing somebody who sounds like Noam Chomsky. The thrill is gone. Plus, it's about ten o'clock in the evening by this time, and happy but exhausted, it's time to see what exactly is happening to me. I let the question and the feelings linger.

What is the appeal? What is the deal?

Clothes make the man Yeah, yeah, whatever. I know the phrase but this is something entirely different. It's more than that. Deeper. It isn't like they made The Man, but made me some Other Man. Or as Eddie Vedder says, a Better Man. This isn't the same vibe of "I look good today." A great haircut doesn't provide this kind of rush. A shirt that fits perfectly in a dressing room doesn't elicit this level of self-confidence. I can't remember a time when that critical chorus, always finding the worst attributes of my face and body, has been silenced for so long.

It's like my whole body feels what it is wearing and goes, *Finally! Something I can relate to.* But am I some vinyl-wrapped, closeted S&M lothario? Because that's how I feel. I feel like, strangely enough, myself in this fucking outfit.

This isn't like I was looking at myself and admiring how great I looked, though I was doing plenty of that. I don't just look great.

I *am* great.

When push comes to shove, despite all the petty and prominent insecurities, I believe I have a fairly healthy ego. But suddenly, in this moment, I feel as if that was the most gargantuan lie I'd ever told myself . . . and I am capable of some self-deceptive whoppers. I've never felt this way before.

I haven't just worked out or ended some cleansing diet, but I feel different inside. I feel stronger, sexier. My spine isn't coated in steel but it feels like it. More than that, it shows. I am standing taller, less slouch. My legs are solid and strong, but I feel sinewy and graceful at the same time. My arms feel like they could grab on to that pull-up bar in the hall and go at it for an hour. The junk in the trunk has proven irresistibly spankworthy and the front view is equally impressive without looking like the cover of *Sticky Fingers*. Then, a dread washes over me:

I might not feel the same way when I take the clothes off.

Then the weirdest notion just floats right in front of me, like someone else lobbed the thought my way. And I get it.

This must be why people cosplay.

I gotta be honest. Sometimes I feel guilty for working so long in anime when I don't have an obsessive, passionate love for the art form. I like it and I do a great job, but there are people who *love* it. They really get into it and they would love to be around the stuff to the level and amount of time I was. I didn't quite understand that. What's worse is I never really asked about their desire or *why* they got into it so much. They're just so different than I am—or so I thought—that I couldn't fathom they'd come up with an answer for me. It was the same way with cosplayers. I would stand off, from afar, and just wonder about them.

Why are they doing that?

I didn't think I was judging at the time but looking back at it now, I realize I must have been. Wasn't I? Looking down on them for playing dress up, thinking they must not be very happy with themselves, which is why they feel the need to dress up as someone else. I know that's not fair and probably just the opposite. They're probably very comfortable with themselves which is *precisely* why they do it. Maybe they have *superior* self-esteem.

What if it's more along the lines that they know themselves so well they're totally aware that the usual off-the-rack clothing isn't for them? That they know this every time they shop? These costumes they wear are more suited to their personality? Maybe for you it's trying on a cardigan at the Gap and thinking, *Yes, this is me to a T. This is me exactly.* But for them the Gap almost feels like drag, or a uniform they're forced to wear. But when they put on a breastplate and hold a sword or they wear some kind of custom tunic and a neon wig, that's when they feel at home.

It's after ten and I'm wondering if I'm going to ever stop eye-gasming or will I just pass out eventually, turning the ensemble into my new special pj's.

Then I receive a text.

Like I said, I don't go out Saturday nights. And most texts after ten o'clock are, well, booty calls.

So I am stoked! And this is one lucky booty caller.

I look at the phone, see the ID, and...*thud.*

Bobby. Not a fuckbuddy, just a friend. We text:

What's up? What are you doing?

Just at home. Threw a shower for a friend of mine today so tired from that what's up?

I'm with Nelson. Tim's outta town. Come over and go out with us.

No thanks. I'll p . . .

The phone rings. It's Bobby calling me from Nelson's house.

Nelson is a bodybuilder. His partner Tim is a psychiatrist. A psychiatrist who's built like a body builder. Bobby is a boy toy from Nebraska or some horrible straight state prone to hate. Nelson and Tim met Bobby online years ago, I believe through Nelson's charity work. Very quickly Nelson became Bobby's shoulder to lean on, preventing his soul from dying a slow death of loneliness in small-town America. Nelson and Tim talked and they threw Bobby a lifeline: if he wanted to get outta there and build a life for himself here, he could move in with them until he carved out his own space. Sure enough, that's what happened.

It took a while for him to finish school and find a job he liked. Eventually Bobby got on at the post office. And as everyone else who comes into Nelson's orbit, Bobby, too, acquired a bodybuilder physique. Truly, that whole crew looks as if they're sculpted. Weekdays they look painfully straight, but they're *tres gay* on Saturdays, going out to the city's oldest and most formidable leather bar, The Ripcord.

"Come with us," Bobby semi-slurred over the phone. "Tim's outta town and we're going to Ripcord."

"You're drunk."

"Well, yeah! Come on. Come with."

I have to admit I am totally flattered by this out-of-nowhere invite. To this day I have no clue how it came about, how my name even floated into the conversation. They're actually friends of a friend and we see each other at birthday parties, maybe an event or two, but we don't hang out. So this request to come barhop with them is such an anomaly I halfway think they're punking me.

"Thanks for the invite, but it's late I'm gonna stay in."

Even as the words come out of my mouth, my regret is palpable. Still, my finger moves toward the End button.

"Oh come on. It's Gear Night."

As if I knew what that was.

"What's Gear Night?"

"It's where everyone wears gear," Bobby starts. My silence forces him to explain further. "Baseball uniform. Leather vest. Cowboy hat and Levis. You know, Gear Night. Everybody dresses up in their hottest gear."

I am standing in front of the full-length mirror in my bedroom. Indeed, most of the evening I have been in front of one-size mirror or the other. But I turn my eyes from the phone and look down at my outfit (like I'm not aware that I have been wearing the damn thing since eleven this morning).

This perfect storm is just ludicrous. I tick the list.

I don't go out on Saturday nights.

I don't go out clubbing.

I don't go out clubbing on Saturday nights.

I don't go out clubbing on Saturday nights with a band of bodybuilders.

I don't go out clubbing on Saturday nights with a band of bodybuilders when it's Gear Night.

Am I actually going to have the final nail in this coffin be, "I don't go out clubbing on Saturday nights with a band of bodybuilding brothers when it's Gear Night on the one night I am actually in gear at that very moment?"

Not even I am that stupid.

Besides, with this kind of unbelievable bullshit of coincidence I'm afraid what might happen if I don't. Because right now it seems that God could very well split the sky open, reach down, and physically place me in the fucking bar if He has to.

"I'll be there in ten minutes."

When I walk in the door to Nelson's house, Bobby hugs me and lifts me up off the ground. Bobby then hands me off to Nelson who hugs me tightly and shakes me. This is what it's like when you're the smallest guy and there are a bunch of gym addicts. I weigh barely 145, so it's easy to throw me around like a rag doll. And you look impressive doing it because, hey, you are, after all, strong enough to be throwing around another grown man like he's a toddler.

It takes me about twenty minutes to convince them of the bizarre coincidence of the call, Gear Night, and my already being dressed for the occasion. The only real evidence I can point to is that I've arrived here, fully dressed and ready to roll in just ten minutes.

When we get to the club, the coincidences keep coming. Apparently every homo that I know is at Gear Night, all of them built like football players, all of them very affectionate through alcohol and the surprise of seeing me there, dressed like this. We're all having such a good time catching up that we wind up closing the place down.

It bugged me for days later why that evening resonated so deeply. Why was I so late to this party? I was too embarrassed to ask anybody at the bar about it. And Gear Night isn't some one shot, it's a regular thing. Which means these men grab that one outfit or costume or whatever you want to call it and put it on with some regularity. It's something that makes them feel, well, like themselves.

I remember reading a quote when Michael Keaton was the first rebooted Batman and he was talking about how ridiculous he felt in the costume. Technologically, socially, sexually, we've come a long way since that stiff, restricting cape and cowl. And I have no actual proof of this but I don't think Chris Evans or any of the other superhero actors these days feel ridiculous. I think they feel like they look. Powerful. Sexy. Brave. Fearless. And more than a little adventurous.

I don't frequent conventions and I don't know if I'll have the opportunity to do so. But I know that when I look at a cosplayer, I won't ever see them in the light in which I viewed them before. If they catch me looking, it will be in admiration. Maybe they'll see that I share their secret with them, now that I'm a member of their club. I have a newfound respect for all you freaks who play this way. It's sad, too, that all it took was me trying things your way just once. But discovering I was missing out on something is like saying the charge I got from the outfit was merely sexual. It wasn't limited to that. Something in me changed. It's like I gained something: a knowledge about myself. Through that stupid erotic ensemble, I somehow came to understand myself a little more.

I think so many times we can label ourselves just as we label others, just as the world needs to label us. Sometimes it's just efficient shorthand, to categorize, though we all know there are plenty of others who do it for other reasons. And sure, if we're forced to pick our spirit animal or our personal crest or name our favorite color, we can. But we have to remember not to limit who we are or what we are. We cannot be defined by one descriptor. It's not just incorrect, it's wrong.

Sure, define me by one thing. Put me in that category or box. Color me. Just for the sake of argument, we'll say I'm gray. But I'm not just one tone of that. I'm not one hue. There are countless shades to me.

Maybe even fifty.

APART OF IT

The One and Lonely

IAN SCHRAGER COULD DESIGN A 7/11 AND I'D STAY THERE. HIS once bracingly original, now-ripped-off aesthetic, with its mad fusion of contemporary and quaint, an old-fashioned notion tweaked with impish nouveau interruptions, is right up my design alley. So naturally, when my first trip to New York rolls around—a city I have fantasized about being in since I saw my first grungy 70s flick set in then-seedy Times Square——I make certain I stay at Schrager's The Hudson.

The Hudson Hotel can be noted by its flat, dark façade with what appears to be open windows jutting out of the smooth, imposing walls. A shaft of nuclear yellow shines out from each, a color you get an eyeful of when you find yourself inside, standing at the genesis of two escalators—one heaven-bound, one earth-descending—that vibrate with the same glowing chartreuse hue. This moving staircase lifts you up from the gray streets of New York to a cavernous, verdant lobby with walls of warm red brick, a high, vaulted glass ceiling choked with greenery, and a massive check-in desk—everything illuminated by a giant chandelier, hologram cards of lightbulbs where actual bulbs should be. I am so wide-eyed when I enter the place, those yellow stairs might as well be a brick road on a steep incline and the lobby its destination Oz.

I am in New York to record a DVD commentary with the two lead actors from cult hit *Farscape*, the TV series that basically put the Sci-Fi (as it was then spelled) channel on the broadcast map. Each episode is reported to have cost about a million dollars to produce, transporting the channel light years from the *Lost in Space* and *Twilight Zone* rerun depository they were before. The show was an immediate hit and has already attracted such a fan base that there is a convention to be held in New York, one occurring just before a second con in England, where the show has an even larger following than it has in the States.

I have recorded commentaries with the entire cast for the first six episodes, and when the decision was made to record running commentary for the last two of the first season, the actors were assured that, per their request, I would be conducting the sessions for the final eps as I'd done for the first. The lead actor, Ben Browder, had even hunted down my whereabouts through the company's sales department to ask me personally if I was going to be the producer—a high compliment, obviously. After the convention and before they left New York to fly to London, the Sci-Fi channel is throwing the production a cocktail party at the appropriately otherworldly theme bar and restaurant, Mars 2112. The plans are for me to fly up to New York, record the commentaries, drop by the convention, and attend the party before flying back home to Houston, where I'll begin to edit the best bits from the recording session and pair them to the episodes for their distribution on DVD.

I've fantasized about New York for decades. As a boy I laid in front of the television set, my body prostrate, eyelids curled so far upward they felt like those cartoon roll shutters on a lusty or anvil-banged coyote, my dizzying head cradled in my two upturned palms. To a kid with starry eyes who lived in Texas, there is no more mind-boggling concept than being able to walk out your front door (which is, for all practical purposes, an elevator!) and be whisked outside, where the city and all its bounty lay mere footsteps before you—a wonderland where the convenience stores are called a far more exotic-sounding *bodega*. Where you can just raise your hand like you do in school to ask a question and a yellow car will answer, taking you anywhere you command it to go. Where the streets are more like crowded elevators, every corner packed with so many people the air seems electrified. Where there is a park bigger than my entire suburb, little satellite parks sprouting up everywhere else. Where buildings look like sky-piercing rocket ships waiting to take off. Where a network of trains (underground ones!) move you from here to there, secretly—"there" being, among other places, an amusement park set on a beach. I don't believe in past lives, but the way this seven-year-old kid fell in love with New York the first time he saw the mecca in a movie, I kinda wonder. It seems too weird that this place could hold such a pull when it was nothing like I'd ever known. But now I am finally here, a big-time producer with money to burn, here to hang out with two TV stars in a tricked-out recording studio. To say the flight landed with my tongue hanging out is only a slight exaggeration. If the windows on the plane rolled down, I'm sure I would have gone full dog. Glen Larson could have sketched me.

Unfortunately, I have to return to Houston as soon as possible and edit the recorded tracks together for the upcoming DVD release, thus I'm not able to bang a couple of vacation days on the back end and extend the stay. So my plan is to kick ass on the commentary, swing by the convention, drop by the Sci-Fi channel party, and use every other waking moment I have to explore the city. I am bound and determined to hit the highlights. Not the touristy sites like Statue of Liberty or the Empire State Building. I won't have time for that. But I will be able to put some serious hours into exploring all the streets I've always heard about like Broadway, 42nd, Wall, Avenues 5th and Park. I'll have to sacrifice the snow globes and I ❤ New York T-shirts for souvenirs of the liquid variety from the more nocturnal haunts in town, mainly the Hudson's lobby bar and the Roxy, the infamous nightclub where I am bound and determined to have at least one dance before I leave town.

After my plane lands, just like I imagined when I was a little kid, I raise my hand and a cab calls on me. The farther we drive, the bigger my eyes get, the city spires rising up, visible through the grimy glass of the taxicab. Eventually the cab pulls round Columbus Circle, depositing me in front of the Hudson.

Checking in, keycard in my hand, I begin the journey to my room, and as with all things Schrager, there is a continual array of eye candy along the way. The walls of the elevator are wave-like and the buttons give off a pleasant, moody glow. The floors are punctuated with art. The room may be microscopic in size but it is decked out for maximum cool with a glass window wall to the shower and a bed framed by two boxes on metal arms. On one side of the box, marbled color panels. Flip that around and you reveal your bedside reading lamps. I drop off my suitcase and go to check out the rest of the hotel. I have very little cool, so I'm sure I am rubbernecking through every locale—the library bar with its violet-felt pool table, giant silver dome suspended above it; the communal cafeteria; the ivy-covered terrace outside with its bed-like palettes, the entire space soundtracked to a mix of club music and the buzz of traffic below; and of course, the bar with its floor made of glass, lit from underneath, Phillipe Starck ghost chairs huddled around Jetson-y tables, the ever-present yellow here represented by a large glass box in the middle of the space, an elevator to nowhere; a fallen log stretches almost the entire length of the floor, seats carved out, every odd chair with a wooden ladderback. Alice, meet Wonderland.

And Alice wants a drink.

* * *

The next morning my excitement wakes me early, no need for an alarm clock. I eat breakfast in the cafeteria and take a cab the several blocks away to the studio to get there well before the talent shows up. The studio is housed, like most studios are, in a nondescript, boring building that betrays the complex and costly recording equipment within. After getting to know the recording engineer and the production manager, I lay out how I want the session to run, familiarize myself with the setup, and wait for the two actors to arrive. They arrive together and early: the series lead, Mr. Browder, and his love interest on the show, Claudia Black.

Ben is Midwestern good-old-boy handsome, with an agreeable manner, a rock-hard, gym-trained body, twinkling eyes, and an easy smile. The kind of guy who'll go in for a handshake but pull you into a tight, slap-on-the-back hug. He's very much like his character on the show—quick-witted and charming. Claudia is slender yet shapely, with shampoo commercial raven-hued hair and a face that's all high cheekbones, flashing green eyes, and a brilliant smile. She moves with a feminine elegance yet admits to being very much "a dork" which makes her all the more endearing, such a rough-and-ready soldier portrayed by a klutzy girlie-girl. We have not seen each other since the day we recorded the commentaries in L.A., months ago, yet they treat me as if I'm an old friend.

After some getting reacquainted small talk, they are ushered into the recording booth together and seated before the microphone and the screen they'll be using to watch the episodes. I take my place at a console near my own mic that I'll use to prompt them during the session, suggesting things to comment or elaborate on—which, lucky for me, isn't very often at all. We record a commentary for the first episode and take a break for lunch. After some time for each actor to return phone calls and texts, they are back in the booth to record the second ep. This time I produce a bottle of champagne. There is, after all, reason to celebrate, as the show had been picked up for another season. Most occasions when I recorded a commentary I have libations for the actors, not that most actors need any Dutch courage or liquid encouragement. But it's a nice gesture that makes them feel appreciated and takes some of the pressure off they might feel at having to fill out a solid hour of speech and not looking like they're struggling with things to say.

The second session goes as well as the first—if a little livelier—perhaps due to the champagne, and I have more than enough material to make two commentaries. I make arrangements for the masters to be FedExed back to Houston, thank the engineer for a great job, and Ben, Claudia, and I walk out together. On the street I ask someone to take a picture of the three of us before we each go our separate ways, saying we'll see each other at the cocktail party since the fans will probably be taking up all their time at the convention.

Me, I am not a fan of the show. Not at first, at least.

The studio had acquired the home-video rights to the show after the president of the company met one of the executives with the Henson Company at MIPCOM in Cannes. MIPCOM is an annual global marketplace for content and where, despite only having a track record in anime, the company secured the home-video rights to distribute *Farscape* in English-speaking territories. Since it would be the company's first crack at non-anime entertainment, the project had a certain pressure and prestige associated with it, and it was decided without much discussion that one of the co-founders in the company would take charge of it and be the property's producer—recording the commentaries, writing the packaging text, working with Henson on whatever other DVD extras they decided to include with the release. I was vaguely aware of the project, but was more than content sticking with producing anime as I'd done for the previous two years. Which is what I was in the middle of doing one day when I was walking from my recording studio to my seldom-used office and the president of the company, a man who had the ability to go from Everything's Fine mode to All Hands On Deck emergency-drill sequence in a blink, stopped me. My office was perilously close to his, and when I said hello to his secretary, Anna, he must have heard me, and he burst out of his office. His face was flushed, his Red Bull-fueled speech rapid, and his beady eyes as wide as was possible for them to be.

"You're going with us to L.A.!"

"I am?"

You see, somehow, at the last minute, management (read: he) had second thoughts about who was to go and record with the cast for the DVDs. Matt, the man initially selected had a tendency, at least within our walls, to be more than a little condescending in his demeanor. He was also, putting it delicately, a little unpolished.

"You are," John confirmed.

"Are you talking about that *Farscape* thing?"

"Yes!"

"I thought Matt was doing it."

"Matt's not doing it," he pulled me aside. "I can't take Matt to meet the Henson people. I can't let Matt hang around the cast all day. I need you to do it."

"But I don't know that show."

"What do you need?"

"To see the episodes, for one," I stated the obvious, my voice laced with more than a little sarcasm. "When do we leave?"

"We leave Thursday."

Two days from now. Jesus.

"You're kidding."

"Anna's already booked your flight."

I stopped feeling sorry for myself immediately at the mention of his poor secretary. She's the one who has to live with him all day. I only get him in occasional red alerts like this.

"I'm in the middle of a show," I stressed.

"We'll put it on hold. I'll talk to Mike. We'll move the release date."

Mike is the sales guy. And moving a release date is a big deal. That never happens.

"Okay then," I surrendered. "Let me get with production, have them make VHS of the masters from season one. I'll have them shipped to my hotel in L.A. and I'll watch as many as I can before we record on…"

"Friday."

"Oh my god!"

"We're only recording six episodes," he said. He seemed to think this made my life easier.

"I don't care. I don't know this show *at all*! I'm not gonna walk in there like some dumbass. I need to know that show like the back of my hand. I'm going to be asking them to come up with shit to say for a solid hour. Six times! Commentaries can get lame fast. I don't want that to happen with these. And you don't either. Not the first time we're stepping out from anime's shadow. We gotta be careful with this shit."

"Good! See? I knew you were the right one for the job!"

Yes, as of about ten minutes ago.

"Get with Anna and she'll make the arrangements."

When I got with Anna, the weight of the situation started to wear on me. So when she asked me where I want to stay, I told her the Chateau Marmont, the celebrity epicenter for everything from overdoses to magazine interviews to movie deals. I figured if I got drafted into this, I was going to have a nice dugout to hole up in. In less than an hour, I had my reservation and the promise of a VCR waiting in my hotel room. Now all that remained was to fly out there and cram in about twenty-four hours of *Farscape* viewing in about a twenty-two-hour period. And to be honest, I wasn't looking forward to it.

Just because I am in anime doesn't mean I'm a science fiction fan. And the Sci-Fi Channel is far down the dial and the network barely on my radar. I'd heard of the show. But to me *Farscape* was just some weird, vaguely foreign-seeming TV series featuring muppets that were just more Monster and less Cookie, like the Jim Henson Company was famous for. Now I was going to have to become a scholar of the show and spend the twelve hours right after my graduation chatting up the cast about all things *Farscape* and sound like I knew what I was talking about. So I red-eyed out to L.A., arriving only shortly after my tapes did. As I was checking in, an extremely tall man came to stand beside me at the front desk. I craned my neck up. Liev Strieber. I wasn't in town an hour and already: celebrity sighting. Welcome to L.A.!

As I was watching *Farscape* over room service, I found the show was, yes, weird but, surprisingly, pretty good. The storylines were interesting and it had crackerjack plotting. Scenes were well-acted and the special effects were an impressive mix of both top-of-the-line CGI and good old-fashioned practical. There were moments where the wealth of Australian accents reeks of an international production, as some shows can, but it wasn't off-putting to my painfully American-TV-watching palate. I got to episode six, the last episode I'd be recording a commentary for the next day. Part of me was tempted to just stop right there. It had been a whirlwind getting here, it was late, and I had to get up early to be at the recording studio. Who could blame me?

Okay, first things first. *Farscape* is about an astronaut who gets sucked into a wormhole and lands in another part of the galaxy, taken aboard a ship that's alive, like a big interstellar whale you can pilot like a boat. It even has a pilot on board—a multi-armed, helmet-head-shaped alien that's grafted to the ship itself. This character is portrayed by a giant muppet. This leviathan has been hijacked by what are basically a bunch of convicts escaping a Nazi-like regime called the Peacekeepers. One of these obedient soldiers was somehow on the ship with the escaping criminals and the regime has deemed her irreversibly contaminated, so she's on the list now too. She's reluctantly on the run with the others—a blue, bald-headed Zen priestess named Zahn, a Klingon knock-off warrior called D'argo, and an arrogant asshole, once-a-ruler-of-his-own-world-and-now-pissed-off-he's-a-fugitive named Rygel. He's played by another muppet. This muppet gimmick, by the way, works surprisingly well, mostly due to the pitch-perfect performers handling the voice work and the sturdy mix of animatronics and puppeteering that goes into bringing these creatures to life.

So the poor, pop-culture-spouting astronaut has to navigate all these various species that are only getting along because they have to, and trying to get these Peacekeepers to leave him alone, which they won't, because when he popped out of the wormhole, his ship killed a Peacekeeper commando's brother so the surviving brother isn't just after the escaped prisoners, he's out for revenge, too.

Got all that?

After a few seconds of deliberation, I grabbed another tape and shoved it in the VCR. Watching six I could probably get by. I hate just getting by. If I have to do something, I'd like to at least think I *tried* to master it.

Now, before this moment, *Farscape* was pretty much just a *meh* space-opera caper punctuated by snappy, rat-a-tat-tat dialogue and an impressive battery of special effects sequences. Nothing to write Earth about. Thank God I put episode 7 in. Because episode 7 changed *everything*.

See, all these freaks desperately want to get to their far-flung home worlds. So badly do they want this, they'll do *anything* to get there. They'll even endure a six-inch-long needle stabbing into one of their open eyeballs to do it. And, no, this sequence doesn't cut away, you have to watch this sadistically long needle slice right into the poor Peacekeeper girl's eyeball. And even though it's a special effect, it's a good one, shown in all its queasy glory. The whole sequence is so uncomfortable to watch, I swear my dick shriveled up and receded into my groin and I instantly developed a needle phobia that, thanks to *Farscape*, is still with me to this day. So when this maniac doing this little bit of eye surgery says he can get them back home, they're all "no problem, how much?" But he begs off. He doesn't want money. All he wants for his services is a sample of DNA from the ship's alien-but-definitely-alive pilot. His arm will suffice. They see this as nothing more than a mild inconvenience.

CUT TO:

The Zen priestess, the warrior, the despot, and the Peacekeeper chick all *sawing one of Pilot's arms off* while he screams for them to stop, stop, it hurts. Their glib justification? He has several arms left over. It'll grow back. Eventually.

Cue the buzzsaw sounds.

I was slack-jawed. Forget that this was a TV show and they were doing this to what is basically a tricked-out mega-muppet. The scene was horrific, and it was coming off the previously reigning champ of disturbing images, the needle-in-the-eye bit. The voice actor playing Pilot sounded like he was actually being dismembered and when the camera zoomed in for a closeup on all his fellow shipmates carving him up like he's their Thanksgiving turkey and everyone wanted the wing, their faces showed determination, disregard, bloodlust, and nonchalance. Zero compassion. It was a sad comment on humanity, alien though it may be. These were the heroes we were supposed to identify with, to root for. And they were assholes! It was clear right then and there this show had little regard for some of the regular tropes of sci-fi. This was no happy, campy *Star Trek*. This wasn't a loyal cadre of officers. They were suspect players who were self-serving at best, backstabbing (or dismembering, rather) at the worst. None were truly trustworthy no matter how much they needed each other. It was obvious when push came to shove and one of them got in their way, they'd shove 'em out an airlock. No wonder this thing had such a huge cult following. It was wicked. It was addictive. Creator Rockne O'Bannon is just *this* side of genius. I fell in love with it.

A few hours later, I'd seen more than enough episodes to conduct a cogent commentary interview from everybody in the cast, but here I was shoving another tape in the hungry VCR promising myself just *one* more. It wouldn't be the first time an addict checked into the Chateau Marmont. (Look how well I fit in in Hollywood!) By 6:00 in the morning, I'd watched all twenty-four episodes and felt I knew as much about the show as a layman could know. There was just enough time for a disco nap before I had to be at the studio, but I didn't care. I could sleep when I got home. Right now there was a job to do. And it just turned into a fun job at that. Now that I'd seen the show, I naturally wanted to rehash it with someone. Who better to do it with than the people who made it?

The next day at the studio, I met the cast and there was not a diva in the bunch. Everyone was friendly, professional, and genuinely happy to be doing what was basically unpaid extra work for us—the little company that was prescient enough to seek out the show and make a bid for home distribution. A week or so later, a few members of the cast sent me handwritten notes saying how much they enjoyed the experience and working with me. Even better, the Henson people were thrilled with the results. I was hailed a hero, even though I didn't do anything except say "recording" and ask them a couple of questions when they ran outta things to say. The cast and the engineer did all the work. Nevertheless, when time came around for the last episodes of season one to be released on DVD, the Henson company was so pleased with the first batch that they wanted to end the slate of releases with another commentary for the last two episodes. It was decided that the show's two main leads, Browder and Black, would record the commentaries. We reserved a New York studio the same time the show was on hiatus and they were both in the city for the convention . . . and now you're all caught up.

Outside the studio, I tell Ben and Claudia I'll see them at the cocktail party but probably not at the convention, what with all the fans wanting their attention and I've already had my generous turn. As I watch them drive off in their cab, I smile, knowing I've done a great job and because I am so thankful they were both so nice. I really like Ben. But my camaraderie with Claudia is stronger. (We wind up being friends for years.)

Now I am all alone. In the best city in the entire world. And basically I am off work until my plane takes off. I am elated. Someone could mug me and beat the shit outta me and I would think it merely a great touristy moment, the only downside being I wasn't able to take a picture of our meeting. I skip the cab and walk the several blocks back to my hotel with an honest-to-God spring in my step. I decide to have a drink in the sexy Hudson bar, and that formally starts my becoming a part of New York, New York.

* * *

It's only three in the afternoon so I'm the only one in the bar. The bartender is a friendly redhead, the cocktail waitress a young African-American. Red is gorgeous and the waitress striking, looking barely old enough to drink drinks let alone serve them. Everyone at the Hudson is beautiful. Even the bellmen. (One was Matt Bomer, if that gives you any idea.)

So when the beautiful redheaded bartender buys me a drink and the equally striking African-American waitress asks me to join them at the bar instead of sitting out here at a satellite table, writing in my notebook, I of course close the notebook.

We have a really good time, the three of us. But as the bar begins to fill with people, I realize it's time for me to go. Like a goon, I ask if I can take a photograph with them, my first friends met in New York. They flag down one of the waiters and make him take the pic. When I ask if they'll be working any other days while I'm here, they both tell me they are, day after tomorrow. Maybe I'll be able to see them again before I leave. I go up to my tiny hotel room, change for dinner, return downstairs to the Hudson cafeteria, and enjoy the best glam macaroni and cheese I've ever eaten in my life. I then go back up to the room and call it an early night.

The next day I hit the convention and, damn, are those actors popular. There aren't very many people dressed up, like they would be at an anime convention or at a *Star Trek* one, but they seem just as dedicated as an otaku or Trekkie. After I put in my appearance, I take off and play tourist.

On my last day in town, since the Sci-Fi party isn't until six or so, I scour the city. I'm not a big walker at home, but in New York I'm like a senior citizen at the mall, trekking for miles on foot. It's nothing for me to walk from the hotel on 51st street to wind up on 1st. I might be a little thirsty, but I won't be tired.

I get back to the hotel in time to relax a little before the party. I shower and dress and head down to the Times Square tourist trap, Mars 2112, which is just a short walk from my hotel.

Mars is located at the bottom of a sunken plaza in front of the Paramount Plaza building at Broadway and 51st. A giant twenty-two-foot saucer-shaped space ship is frozen in mid-flight before the entrance below the street level. You take a "transporter" to get into the club and restaurant, and once you arrive "on Mars," you continue your stellar journey on industrial catwalk over a lake of simulated lava. Volcanic-looking red rock walls give the place an alien mine-on-Mars feel, the geological terrain illuminated in fire-yellow lanterns and flame-red accent lights. Wide gaps in the prop walls reveal animated star fields and computer-generated Martian landscapes. Waiters are made up to look like aliens and the cocktails are christened mars-tinis and cosmos-politans. It's all very kitsch yet somehow manages to be *this* close to cool at the same time.

I say brief greetings to the cast, all of whom, except for Ben and Claudia, I haven't seen since L.A. But everyone else knows someone at the party so I am quickly the odd man out. Probably seeing I am uncomfortable and a little lost, Claudia rescues me by calling me to her table.

"Sit down, darling," she purrs in her slightly accented voice. "Join us." She introduces me to the girl with her as her best friend, Annalise, in town from Australia.

Claudia goes on and on about how great a producer I am; I tell them my story about cramming twenty-four hours of *Farscape* viewing.

"He knows the show better than we do," Claudia says.

Because it's my last night in New York I'm not going to stay long at the *Farscape* party, so when I tell my companions I want to take in a little nocturnal sightseeing before leaving town, they completely understand. Claudia says she has to meet someone who is coming to the party so she offers to walk me out.

As we walk away from Mars, I ask about Claudia's life and her relationships. She says she is single but has struck up a connection with one of the guest stars on the show. He is coming to the party that night to meet her and she is filled with that first-date rush of nerves and excitement. We hug goodbye, and since he is moments away, she stays outside to greet him.

Before I leave, it begins to lightly rain and I turn around from the upper level and look past the flying spaceship to this beautiful woman standing there in the falling drops, waiting in the rain. It is a little melancholy and a little beautiful and I linger there a moment, just watching her, before turning around and going on my way.

* * *

"Hi, do you have any drugs?" is what I say.

It is 11:00 and I am at the Roxy, the dance mecca I've vowed to see before I leave. And I want to see it "enhanced."

It's not surprising the guy I'm talking to gives me a *Fuck off, freak* look and then leaves me standing there in the club alone. But I am so desperate to make a connection, I do not let this dampen my resolve. I want something to alter my mind, despite all my little gray cells being sufficiently elevated. It is my last night in New York and I want a blow out. So imagine my surprise when the second person I ask has quite a different response.

He is in a group of four, all in their late twenties, all attractive, each one moving to the music, watching the dance floor as they talk with each other in loud voices that barely carry over the driving club music. They are off to one side of the cavernous club, a wonderland of swirling lights with enormous bars, hundreds of trendies, and, off the dance floor, an oasis furnished with sofas, all sitting beneath the sails you usually find covering tables at outdoor patios. It is gay night, just my luck, and I figure-slash-hope I can score some dope from a member of my tribe. I have just enough chutzpah to ask exactly one more person, and if I come up empty-handed again, I'll just take it as a sign I'm meant to experience the Roxy straight—despite how gay the club is.

"Hi, I'm Steven," I begin and immediately the group falls silent. I don't think any of them knows which one of them I'm addressing so they all wait for sufficiently elongated eye contact. "I know this is going to be a real weird request to ask but this is my first time in New York and I don't know anybody and I'm looking for some, you know...stuff."

"Where are you from?" one guy yells over the pulsing music.

"Houston," I scream back.

"No shit! We're all from Dallas!"

We all laugh at the bald coincidence and I am relieved that my request doesn't get an immediate brush off.

"We have K," he tells me.

"What's K?" Just because I am looking for drugs doesn't mean I'm a connoisseur.

"Special K. You know."

"No, I don't. What's it do?"

"It'll turn all this up to about eleven," he tells me. And seconds later we are in the bathroom stall together, unwrapping a carefully folded piece of tin foil that reveals a flattened pile of off-white powder. I snort as instructed, hang out with him in the stall for a little bit—small talk, you know—and then exit the bathroom, leaving them to their own devices and me to check out the enormous danceteria till the drugs kick in.

Thankfully, when they do, I am within arm's length of that living-room-like, parasail-covered rest area. The drug's power blindsides me and I reach out for the back of the couch closest to me and sit on its back, watching the dance floor lights become more luminescent, ever liquid. I am way too high for my own good so I stay there, landlocked on the couch for what must be an hour, wondering the whole time, *What have I done?*

After the initial high calms down to a manageable level, my eyes land on a couple on the dance floor. My gaze may have locked there because after a few moments of staring at them—stupidly, I'm sure but apparently not so stupidly they don't motion me to come join them. Because I am high, I do.

As the track we are dancing to segues into the next, we keep moving and continuing to dance, changing partners to leave the lone other to move to the beat of his own drummer, only to rejoin us and make us a trio once more. It is more slippery sexual than gropingly pornographic, not that anyone else on the floor notices or cares how handsy we get.

After a few songs, I am sweaty and thirsty and beg off to get a drink.

"Wanna come back to our place?"

The invite is both surprising and flattering, but a three-way tourist attraction isn't something I'm up for, despite all evidence and novelty to the contrary, so I thank them and they soldier on, unfazed.

As the night winds down to about one in the morning, I take my last glance at the mecca of music and moving bodies and say goodnight to the Roxy. I leave feeling that I've taken as big and selfish a bite out of the Big Apple as is possible for a whirlwind three-day work trip. I'm satisfied, but slightly dreading having to get up at sunrise to catch an early flight out.

* * *

I am more than a little hung over the next morning when I wake up, having slept through the hotel wakeup call and my alarm. Realizing I'll never make it to the airport on time, I sigh, chide myself, and then reach for the phone to call the office. I'll have to beg poor Anna to get me another flight. So much for my model employee status.

"Anna Bechtol," she answers. She sounds distant. More emotionally than technically it seems. I shrug it off to my own guilt.

"Hey, Anna, it's Steven."

"Hey, Steven," she says. Not that she should be thrilled to hear from me, but her recognition holds no real friendliness. It's like she barely knows me. I shrink, thinking she must know why I'm calling and hating me for the inconvenience I'm about to put her through.

"Listen, Anna, I'm not going to make my flight."

"Well, I guess not!" Now she seems to light up.

I don't think my reputation is that bad. I've never missed a company flight before. Very quickly my night at the Roxy is looking like a bad decision all over the place.

"When the plane crashed into the World Trade Center, I had a flash of *Is Steven on that flight?*"

Groggy, but waking up rather quickly now, I ask her what she's talking about.

As she tries to tell me, I come to sit at the edge of the bed. My hand reaches out to the television set. I turn it on and it flares to life.

I see what is happening, but it doesn't register. There are the Twin Towers, one of them bisected with a collar of thick smoke roiling upward to the higher floors. Slowly and steadily what appears to be another plane comes into frame.

Suddenly, the second tower explodes into a burst of flame and smoke.

I say something. *Oh my God*, or something like that. But Anna doesn't hear me. The line is dead.

Everything that happens afterward are only slight memories, fragments that go on repeat every September:

I remember sitting on the bed watching the coverage in my hotel room for hours. I don't leave the side of the bed, not to get a drink of water, not to piss, not to shower, nothing. Eventually I put on some clothes and walk to the elevator. There are four Germans in the lift with me, all laughing, having a great, touristy time. I think they must not have been watching the news, they don't know. My shellshocked self allows them to leave the elevator first. They giggle and trot through the lobby and disappear down the escalator. Numbly, I walk up to the front desk. I tell them I won't be checking out as planned. They ask me how long I'll be extending my stay. I tell them I don't know.

I remember walking in the streets that are not as crowded as they had been previously, very un-New York. I wander aimlessly, passing perfectly fine lunch spots—food the reason for finally leaving my hotel room—but enter none of them. Slowly, in the crowd, I notice what look disturbingly like ghosts. They're human, obviously, but they're covered in white powder. Some walk hurriedly, others walk like most of us are walking. Like zombies.

I remember going into a sandwich place where everyone is watching the TV above the bar. I order soup and a sandwich. I take three spoons of the soup, two bites of the sandwich, I pay the bill, and I leave.

I remember waiting in the hotel lobby with other stranded guests, each of us in a line to use the only phone working in the hotel, the pay phone. I remember calling my family, telling them I'm alright.

I remember trying to find Claudia and Ben, the only souls I know in New York. I don't want to be alone. I never reach them. I don't know what hotel they were staying in, nor what alias they are checked in under.

I remember wandering the streets.

I remember a call for blood donations. I try to give blood but they don't take it because I'm gay, a holdover policy I don't know about, a practice begun during the AIDS crisis. I hear there is a call for toiletries, for the hordes of rescuers and others working at Ground Zero. I look in several pharmacies until I at last find one that has some toothbrushes left on the otherwise bare shelves. I purchase all they have, find one of the donation points, and deposit my shoddy offering, convincing myself that if I could do more, I would. Like everyone, I feel vulnerable, helpless.

I remember for two days my time is filled by waiting in the phone line, watching the news coverage of the incident, and wandering aimlessly, waiting for the airports to begin allowing planes to fly once again.

I remember going to the bar looking for the redheaded bartender and the cocktail waitress. I ask about them. Neither came in to work. I am filled with horror, but convince myself they're both alright. I pray they're both alright.

I remember two days later when my boss tells me to just drive back. Find a rental car and just get home. He is very comforting and after hanging up the phone, I go to my hotel room and consider this.

I remember finding a small bookstore. Once inside, I locate a section of geographical reference books and a cache of maps. I take two, one of New York and one of the United States. I sit down on the floor, unfolding them, pulling the paper of jagged lines and colored quarters closer to my face. With my finger, I trace a line from New York to Houston. Half the country. Still, I begin to think this is feasible.

I remember standing in line at the rental car office, obviously not the only one with this plan in their heads. I remember the shock I feel when, after I am given my keys, the clerk makes an announcement.

"That's it, ladies and gentlemen. We have no more cars. I repeat: We have no more rental cars available at this location," he tells us. I look at the keys in my hand. The last car. The line groans. I turn around.

"I'm going to Houston. If anyone is headed toward Texas, you're more than welcome to hitch a ride with me. Really."

"Swing by Chicago?" a man in line asks me. I pause, guilt washing over me, selfishness controlling my answer.

"No," I tell him. "I'm sorry."

I remember being nervous about driving in New York traffic, but everything goes slowly and smoothly. All traffic moves strangely, as if through water.

I remember listening to the radio without changing the station. I remember stopping finally in Tennessee to spend the night in a Holiday Inn.

I remember being pulled over the next day by a Tennessee state trooper. I remember him coming up to my window. I remember thinking he's really handsome.

"License and registration, please," he orders quietly.

Wordlessly, I fumble for what he wants. I hand him my license.

"It's a rental car," I say. My throat seizes. I feel emotion rising from the whole of my body, crawling up my throat, filling my face.

"Do you have any idea how fast you were going?"

I don't remember exactly what I say to him. I only know that it is spoken through an eruption of crying. I know I get out what I can, that I'm just coming from New York, that I was stuck there for three days, that I managed to get the last car in Manhattan, and I don't know how fast I was going, I don't know. He pauses slightly, my emotion bringing understandable discomfort, a loss for words. He doesn't know what else to say so he answers the question for me.

"Ninety-six."

I remember that I continue crying and he somehow gets me out of my car. We sit on the hood of my car and he stays quietly with me until I manage to stop sobbing. When I tell him I'm sorry, so sorry, he tells me it's alright and tells me just to sit here. I obey until what seems like a very long time until I tell him, at last, that I'm okay. He escorts me back to my car. The steering wheel feels huge in my hands. He does not give me a ticket.

"Drive safely," he tells me. I tell him I'm just going to sit here in my car for a while, if that's alright with him. He says it is.

"Don't speed."

I remember I don't obey him.

I remember how there are many speeding cars, all with different license plates than the state I am in. Those drivers with plates from their own state continually move to the slow lane, as if they realize who we all are, all of the people stranded in different cities around the country because all flights are cancelled. It's like everyone is being overly courteous. If there is rage, it isn't on the road but directed elsewhere.

I remember, after another full day of driving, pulling into the parking space behind my brownstone. I go in through my back door. I call my parents, as instructed, now that I am home. I think about calling my children. They are too young for this. We are all too young for this.

I remember thinking this wasn't the New York I wanted to be a part of. Not this. Not like this.

I remember going out the front door to get my pile of mail.

I remember noticing that my bike that I left in the hall has, during this elongated stay away, has been stolen by someone.

I remember falling to the ground.

I remember wondering if he feels guilty now.

THE LIST

The Punisher

You're a terrible person.

What kind of man are you that you think the things you do? You're disgusting.

You can't even remember your daughter's birthday.

You're so lazy.

You only perform those good deeds of yours because you're looking for some kind of karmic reward. Well, it doesn't work like that.

You're so ugly. Look at your face.

You can't even drag your lazy ass to the gym every day. No wonder you're out of shape.

I can't believe you're groaning about having to take the dog out. It's just a couple of times a day. And you don't even have the dog over that much.

That's all you're giving? What a miser.

You just can't forgive them, can you? What does that say about you as a person?

You're a lousy friend.

That was such a stupid thing to say.

You're being ridiculous.

You're a hypocrite.

This is awful.

What's the matter with you?

You can be so mean-spirited at times, you know that?

How you think about other drivers on the road. You're so petty.

Well that just isn't good enough.

Quit giving so much advice to people. Can't you just shut up and just listen?

I wish you'd never been born.

Speaking of friends, you're not as good a friend to your friends as they are to you.

You're selfish.

Would it kill you?

You look so old.

I can't believe you said that.

How many times must I tell you?

You're gonna pay for that some day.

Things would be better off without you.

You just can't let it go.

Just shut up, will you?

What makes you think you're so much better than that person? You know you're worse.

He's never going to call you back. Why should he?

Stop being so judgmental.

Quit comparing yourself to others. You know you don't measure up.

How can you even show your face in public?

You're setting a terrible example.

You're a bad Christian.

You feel guilty all the time. Why do you think that is? Because you *are*.

You're too needy.
You deserve everything that happens to you.
Did you remember to say thank you?
You'll get yours, don't you worry.
You didn't even send them a card.
Yes, it is true.
You're the worst.
Couldn't you have put a little more thought into this?
You're so disrespectful. That's why you're late all the time.
You've lost your mind.
You can't be trusted.
You talk too much.
This is never gonna pan out.
You should be ashamed of yourself.
Of course they forgot about you.
You never know when to quit, do you?
You deserve to be punished.
You're pathetic.
You've got some nerve.
You should just quit while you're ahead.
Everyone is so much smarter than you.
When will you get it through that thick head of yours?
All your best days are behind you.
You make me sick.
What were you thinking?
You know what you did.
Would it kill you just to smile a little more?
Did you see the way they just looked at you?
How can you even look yourself in the mirror?
Do you really think things are going to get better?
You deserve what you get.
You're not gonna make it.
What do you have to say for yourself?

You're such a whiner.
That looks terrible on you.
You'll get yours one day.
You'll never learn.
No one cares what you have to say.
Things are not going to get any better.
You're so stupid.
Stop being that way.
I wouldn't do that if I were you.
How could you?
That's gonna come around and bite you on your ass.
Quit feeling sorry for yourself.
I can't believe you did that.
Faggot.
You have it so much better than everyone else.
Stop thinking you're so superior.
They really meant that.
You're lucky you've gotten this far.
You should just call it a day.
You're not trying hard enough.
You'll never amount to anything.
Why are you like that?
You're not worthy.
So that's what you think?
They're all laughing at you.
You'll never change.

Warning:

The following story contains adult language and graphic sexuality.

Sensitive readers may want to proceed to the next story.

INTERIOR DESECRATOR

The Other Man

It is early in the morning and I'm at the end of another sleepless night. I am at that waking weakness point. My body's too alert for sleep, my brain too fatigued to do anything truly productive. Watching television doesn't seem appealing. I wouldn't be able to focus on a book. So I pick up my phone and log on to Grindr. I'm not necessarily looking for anyone, just perusing profiles mostly. I suppose I'm just trying to feel some connection, online, with others like me. But no one person makes me want to contact them, and the whole flesh parade of profiles has long since lost its luster. Still, it's a comfort knowing there are others like me, looking. Existing. I'm ready to log off and maybe make some breakfast when I get a text from "Top." His profile—total top, alpha male, very verbal, NSA—feels like it's practically addressed to me.

July 14
5:21 a.m.
Hey

Hello, Sir.

Great pic and profile
[sends pic]

[pic received]
Thank you Sir!
You're a hot looking fucker. Have any pornographic pics you wanna share?

[sends pics]

[pics received]
Aw hell dude. I'm in.

I'm interested

Your place or mine

Can't host, so if you can

I can host

Very alpha
Hung true 8 thick
And verbal
LOVE guys smaller than me.

Shut up. That will kill me. Verbal alpha
That's the biggest fucking turn on

Very
VERY VERY VERY
I'm a pounder also.

Just coach me through it, walk me through it, or force me to take it, they're all hot ways to fuck

Big rimmer too

I'll hit the showers so I'm squeaky clean for you.

Any other pics?

I'm not a talker but I am a fucking moaner. and grunter. and crier. and whimperer

I love a moaner!!!
[pics sent]

[pics received]
Ohhhhh fuuuuck. I'm nervous now.
Which probably turns you on all the more.
Let me throw you some pics
[pics sent]

[pics received]
You're perfect
Lean, little, grrrr
I'll own you

Yeah, I'm a little thing. You're going to throw me around the room.

I like

I'm probably in way over my head here.

Truly
Small guys are my weakness

So what are my orders top? What do you need me to do besides shower and get ready for you

That all depends on how sub you can get

I have one rule about sex
if somebody's not having a good time just call it
no harm no foul no hard feelings and no drama

Ok
I'm a killer top
So far, you're perfect

What time you looking for?

When are you usually free

I make my own schedule.
Just gimme a little heads up and i'm at your beck and call

Awesome
Kendall here

I mean you got me so turned on I want you over here in half an hour
But I understand. Schedules.
Nice to meet you Kendall
Jesus you're a hot motherfucker

This am I should be free after 8
I need to hit the gym soon
But I'm really really interested

As well as you should be
I'm a hell of a fuck

Hard to find a sane total bottom small framed my age
I can be very nurturing as well
I like sex very passionate
But I also like to caress and cuddle

OK you're starting to look a little too good I'm starting to feel taken

Lol
[pics sent]

I hope you're legit because I'm turned on as fuck

I'm real

[pics received]
Holy fuck
It comes down to chemistry anyway. you and i are actually helpless as far as if anything clicks or not. it's all up to DNA and atoms smashing together.
And us smashing together
[pic sent]

Man I love how lean you are
Little waist
[pic received]
Stop
You're a ginger!!

Not so much on top anymore but below the belt yes I am

You're having my baby
This is a done deal
This is tooooooo good to be true

It probably is
But I say we take a chance.

Just give me what I don't get at home boy

Well I guess I'll have to figure out what that is wont I?

In return I'll treat you like a prince/little whore

That'll be fun decoding that.

What's your name
I want you to whimper mine as I cum

It's whatever you like saying. It's whatever feels
best rolling off your tongue

I love being called daddy

Well I like calling you daddy

NSA is perfect
But if we click I want more

Sounds good daddy

Call me daddy in bed and I'll go Rambo
555-749-0908
Text me if you want

You know that's going to happen

I love being treated like the most important guy in
the world FYI

In case you haven't figured that out yet so far you
are.

Make me feel wanted and special and I'll stay

I get off on that.
That's my yin
Might've found my yang

Miserable at home
I want a reg bf to take my needs out on

I'll make sure this is a nice place for you to hang

Baby that's perfect
Take care of your man

Just tell me how you like it

Be a WIFE
And when I want to fuck you Just say yes daddy

Yes daddy. You should hear me say it now. I have a pretty good voice.

Nice
VERY DEEP HERE

Bet it rises in pitch when we're fucking

Your screen shot pic is perfection

Give it to me daddy. Just go slow at first so you don't hurt me. And we're not rushing

I take care of my property
But when I need to cum, I make it happen

Wife? Can't guarantee that. But I'll be your little bitch maybe

Perfect

Daddy's favorite

Holy fuck
I'm precumming
Truly

Wait til you're here in person

I swear

When I suck your dick

I love deep head

Nice to meet you, Kendall

Cell phone

I'm looking for my Daddy

Hey boy
Was getting my coffee

Well I hope I get to see you today

I'm really damn stoked about this
Yes
Possibly today?

I'm yours today just say when.

Where in the heights?
For reference

Near 10 and shepherd
Modest little casa in the throes of a major renovation

If I skip the gym
Want to this am?

You know I do

Ok
Let's do it

I want you thirty minutes ago and a shower I haven't had yet

Get showered
I want you to sit on my face

Only if you've got sufficient time to have real sex.
No quickie not the first time

I do
I own my own company

We are a dangerous combination

A good fit

My schedule is my own as well.

What's your bed like?

OK so it's 630 now, what time you looking at boss

7:15?

Ok. Hope you take your coffee black. I'm all outta cream

Your ass is all I need

You got it daddy it's yours I will text you when I'm ready with the address

Ok
I'll head that direction around 7
Shower. Now

Yes sir I will text you soon daddy
I'm anxious

We're gonna be fine
Trust me you can trust me
Getting dressed
Be ready

Wrapping up my shower in 5
2618 Alice Circle

Did we used to fuck?
"Big Top"

Holy shit. Like five years ago?
You moved to Colorado
Or some place
Oh fuck I hope I'm not a disappointment
I swear one moment I thought Alpha top? I thought no way

It's me
Oh hell no
I want you

I'm all yours daddy
And if I remember you, this is gonna hurt

On my way

I'll be wearing underwear. You can tear it up if you want

I'm going to tear u up

Can't believe you're fuckin back

Ass up when I walk in

Yes sir

After I get ready, I am in the bed, phone in hand, ready to read the text conversation again while I wait. I stop at the line where he asks me what my bedroom is like. That question passed by me the first time so I didn't answer him. But I think he'll like what he sees.

In the center, a four-poster, silver-gunmetal behemoth of a queen bed. In lieu of a headboard there is a glistening black rectangle of paint on the cappuccino-colored walls. Within this box is a silver steer skull looking down on the bed, its long, curved horns breaking the boundaries of the black shape. At the foot of the bed is a giant array of mirrors in varying sizes and shapes. A large rectangle one in the middle reflects the main of the bed, with several others positioned around it. An antique oval here, a circular convex mirror there. The wall is filled with them. To the right of the bed is a tall mirrored wardrobe. I'd like to say all the mirrors are there for strictly sexual purposes, but that would be a lie. They are there to make the microscopically sized bedroom appear larger than it actually is. The fact that you can see yourself at almost any position on the bed is just a Lucky Strike extra. As I look at myself, I catalogue my flaws.

I remind myself that *he* came on to *me*. He remembered *me*.

God, I am always on the prowl. I'm constantly hungry for the next kill and my mouth salivates at the thought of a new other. Muscles are just tense enough, always ready to pounce. I've always been like this. For as long as I can remember. I'm sure a shrink would say it has something to do with being molested at such a young age, but I don't think so. I was always aware, even before I had sex, that this body was meant for other things, things I hadn't experienced yet but knew were on the horizon. Flesh things. My skin practically crawled at the anticipation of being touched. The older I got, I could feel this energy getting closer. I didn't know exactly what was going to come, but I couldn't wait for it to get here.

I look back at the text. Reading it is a better mood-setter than any porn I could be watching. And I grow more excited rereading every line. Soon, I hear the front door open—I left it unlocked—and I freeze. That adrenaline rush, the fight-or-flight response encoded in my DNA floods my chest, my stomach. I hear the door close and then the floorboards creak with each of his steps. Within seconds, those slow footsteps have stopped. I'm not facing the doorway but I can feel him there. That slightly perceptible change in space that occurs when you know: you're not alone anymore.

He comes into the bedroom. He says nothing. I feel his eyes pan over my body, my bent-over form in the position he requested—ordered?—me to be in. Then I feel two hands on my ass. The skin along my whole body tingles while he rests them there for a minute before gripping the fabric. In one quick move, I hear the *rrrrip!* of cloth as my underwear is shredded in one aggressive tear.

"Oh, fuckin' sweet," he says. His voice is deep, hungry. He takes his fingers and slowly but roughly shoves them inside me. A sound escapes my mouth. Not a gasp, grunt, or groan exactly, more like a combination of all three. He voices his approval, "Nice and tight."

He bows his head and moves near my ass and inhales deeply. Liking what he smells (or doesn't smell—my ass is so clean you'd think I was gonna have a colonoscopy), he begins eating me out, aggressively. After a few minutes, he stands upright again and I move around on the bed to face him. I see him now for the first time and a feeling explodes inside, a rush of recognition.

He's tall, over six feet, with blond hair streaked in lighter blond and gray. His blue eyes are steely, sharp. He's impossibly handsome, with a dimpled cheek and a comic book hero's jaw. He's built like a brick shit house. *Yes. I know this body.*

He strips off his shirt and there is that torso, with its massive chest, well-defined pecs, smooth abs, and muscled arms. He unzips his pants, releasing his cock, enormous and already almost fully erect. I put it in my mouth. He shoves me down on him, hard. I struggle, then submit.

While I gag, he leans over slightly and grabs my ass again. Then he rips the rest of the shredded underwear from my waist. He turns to the side and profiles himself in the wardrobe mirror, and makes me watch while I suck him. He fingers me and after a few moments of this, he lifts me up off my stomach and throws me backward onto the bed. He takes off the rest of his clothes, laying the pants, his boxers, and socks on a chair, shoes beside. He climbs into bed, rolls onto his back, and orders me to serve him.

And I do.

"Turn around," he commands and I obey, straddling him. I am all muffled groans and stifled moans, servicing him while he all but consumes me. This seems to last for an eternity. He slaps my asscheeks three times, hard, and I lift my mouth from his cock and gasp. He then grabs my hips and places them onto his now rock-hard cock. I try to slow him down.

"You're huge and I'm tight," I tell him. But it doesn't matter. Nothing I say is going to change anything, least of all his control of the situation.

"Sit on my fuckin' dick," he commands.

"Yes, Sir." It sounds like a defeat. My hands search for my bottle of poppers.

"You don't need your poppers. Shut up and sit on my dick. Be a bottom."

The slight fingering was inadequate preparation. I'm not lubricated and his cock is barely wet from my mouth. He enters me hard and dry. He has to force it. I almost scream. He purrs his approval.

"Yeah? Yeah?" he asks me, his voice a little higher, teasing. Then, immediately, deep: "Sit on my fuckin' dick," he repeats, this time more sternly. "Man up!"

I struggle to take him in.

"You should see your ass. It's so fuckin' red."

"Easy. Please?"

But he is having none of it. He grabs my hips and pulls me down harder. "Don't you remember how I used to fuck you, little boy?" he asks. "Don't you remember how I used to fuck you?"

"Yes," I moan. "But it's been so fucking long." The sounds of pain and pleasure mingle.

"Like that nice big raw dick in you, huh? Isn't that what you love?" He snarls, "Fuckin' bottom. Fuckin' ginger bottom."

My hand reaches for my penis.

"Don't touch your fuckin' dick," he snaps. Then, softly: "I'll take care of you." He watches the proceedings intently, gives me his appraisal. "Oh, that's so fuckin' pretty."

He never allowed me to grab the lube and he sure isn't going to do it. I have to find a way to lubricate his cock. It hurts too much going in this way. I lift myself off of him and begin sucking him again, wetting his cock with the liquid from my mouth. I drool over him. Anything to get the damn thing wet.

"You're here to satisfy my needs."

His cock now slick with saliva, I climb back on.

"Oh, yeah. Sweet fuckin' ass. Sweet fuckin' ass. Yeah. *Yeah.*"

I start moving.

"Be my ultimate fuckin' bottom," he tells me. He never takes his eyes off the sight. "That's so fuckin' beautiful." Then, quietly but forcefully: "Look at yourself in the mirror."

I turn to the right and, for a second, am taken out of the moment by what I see.

"I can get a little bit of it," I tell him casually, meaning I can catch a glimpse of him going in and out of me. It's the part that sucks about being a bottom. Your view is lousy. "Jesus Christ, you're gigantic."

I am wearing a black muscle shirt. Around my neck, a thin leather necklace. He grabs the leather strip with his right hand and pulls downward, forcing me to take him deeper while he thrusts his hips upward. I respond. Loudly. I can't speak words. All I can do is moan, gasp, cry out with each movement of his hips. I grab the hem of the black muscle shirt I'm wearing. It's like I'm holding onto reins.

"Take off that shirt. I wanna see that lily white skin."

I strip off the shirt.

"Oh, that's so beautiful. Show me how much you enjoy it. Come on, fuckin' take care of me. Show me why I love being a top."

Suddenly, a feeling of power brushes over me. Perspective had changed. I flirt with him.

"You want me to ride you?"

"Yeah, I want you to ride me," he agrees hungrily. "Gimme a show. Show me what you've got."

After riding him for several moments, I reach my hand up and grab the top bar of the metal four poster and pull, lifting my ass off his cock. Then I thrust my hips, the weight of my body suspended so that just the pressure and weight of my ass is resting on him. He enjoys this awhile but then tires of it, and he uses my position to his advantage and swings one leg over my body, so he is at a new angle, thrusting deeper inside of me. Finally, after a few punishing moments, he orders me off the bed.

"Lay on your back."

I have my back to him and, apparently, I don't move fast enough. He grabs the leather collar and shoves me forward.

"I'm goin', I'm goin'," I tell him in a small voice and turn over onto my back. I am now in a position where I can face him. He hooks his hands around my thighs and pulls me toward the edge of the bed. He enters me again.

"God, you're so fucking hot," I tell him, the words barely more than breaths coming out of my mouth. I watch his face, see his gaze turn downward, to where his cock is going into me. A look of satisfaction plays across his face and I watch it change him. "Oh my god."

"What are you?" he asks me, full-throated, staring right into my eyes.

"Your fuckin' bottom?"

He nods. "That's right. I get to breed you any time I want to."

"Yes, Sir," I tell him and his eyes go back to watching his cock enter me. I reach up and move my hands over his firm pecs, fingers pinching his nipples, then rubbing the span of his massive, smooth chest. "Yes, Daddy."

He brings his eyes back to mine.

"You glad I'm back, baby?" he coos. "You glad I'm back?"

"Yes, Sir. I missed you. A lot." I sound like a child.

He moves his body over me, closer to me, like he's going to kiss me. Instead his mouth twists and he spits on me.

"Fuck!" I yell as he starts to pound me harder. "Oh my god…"

Just when I think I can't take any more of this, his thrusts change, becoming more fluid now. He rocks his body left and right. He looks like he's skiing almost and, in a way, he is. My white skin like snow. I am just terrain to be moved upon. And my body will bear his tracks. I can't take my eyes off him.

"Oh yeah," he says, hips swaying. "I'd forgotten what a great fuck you are." He takes his hands from my thighs and moves them down to my feet. "Take these fuckin' socks off," he says and then strips them off of me. He looks at me intensely. Reflexively, my hand reaches down to my cock again. He bats it away. "Get your hands off your cock," he barks. He leans closer as his thrusts quicken. "This is about me. You got it? Always. You cum when I want you to cum."

"Yes, Sir."

We both begin moaning in sync. He closes his eyes at last, throws his head back.

"Oh my god, this ass is so fucking good!"

He grabs my legs and pulls me deeper, harder. I cry out. It makes him fuck me even harder. I gasp for air.

"Take it," he tells me firmly. "Take it. *Take it.*"

"Yes, Sir."

He moves me around to a new position. Another cry.

Then, just like that, his motions change. They become smoother again, less harsh. Aggression leaves him, as easily as if he dropped a piece of clothing. He throws his head back and closes his eyes once more.

"That's so fuckin' nice right there," he says quietly. Sweetly.

"Oh, dude."

"That's so good, baby."

"Oh my god."

"You're so open right now."

"I still feel tight as fuck!" I tell him, amazed at this assessment.

His thrusts become more aggressive. I respond in kind. He slaps me on my ass and it makes a loud, quick *SMACK!* Then, back to closed eyes. Mine remain open, riveted. I memorize every second, every shift in his manner, each look of pleasure that traces along his face. But now I want something.

"I want to suck you," I tell him, unsure if he'll allow it. But we part and he backs up from the bed. I climb off and drop to my knees, taking his hard cock in my mouth again.

"Oh, that's so good." He moans. "Oh fuck, baby, yeah! God, that's the best fuckin' head." He shoves my skull down on him harder. Then he lifts me up and bends me over the bed.

"Holy *shit*."

It's a new position. Every new position brings a different wave of hurt, the process of getting used to his size begins again. I feel my back arching up.

"Put your fucking back down!"

"Oh fuck! Oh god! *Jesus!*" Again, it's all I can muster. It's a slam-dance of pain and pleasure that reduces me to prayers, phrases, pleas.

"Oh, baby, you feel so fuckin' good right now!" He says it almost as a triumph. As if he has brought me to this place where my body is giving him just the kind of pleasure he was seeking.

"Fucking hell your cock is too fucking huge! Oh god!" I say through grit teeth. He grabs the choker around my neck again, pulls.

"Get used to it." He puts his hands on my shoulders, pulling me down onto him even deeper, pounding me ever harder.

"Yes, Sir. Yes, Sir. Yes, Sir."

"You gonna be my bottom?" he asks in that higher pitch, that softer, teasing tone. "You gonna keep that hole perfect for me?"

"Yes, Sir, I promise."

"Keep that waist nice and small?"

I try to keep quiet, but I can't. I bury my face into the mattress. He takes his hand and places it on the back of my head and shoves me even further down into the cushioned top.

"Whose needs are more important?"

"Yours are," I reply, muffled.

"That's right."

"Am I not meeting them?" I ask him, genuinely curious.

As an answer, he curls his arms under mine, puts his hands on my shoulders, and pulls me closer to him. As he thrusts, he whispers in my ear.

"Say 'I'm a whore.'"

"I'm a fuckin' whore."

"Whose whore are you?"

"Your whore."

"*My* fuckin' whore."

"Kendall's fucking whore."

This response seems to satisfy him.

"Stand up."

And with that, he maneuvers me in front of the mirror, his hands on my shoulders. He looks at my reflection and whispers in my ear.

"The last time I was here, I gave you a condom wrapper and told you to keep it as a souvenir. Did you?"

Then he releases me.

I am dumbfounded. I can't believe he remembers it. I can't believe he's asking me. But what I really can't believe is that I *have* kept it. And strangely, thinking I'd never see him again, had just thrown away the torn metallic gold memory a few months ago.

For a moment, our passion is sidelined and, for the first time, we're talking to each other like there's actually a soul inside our shell bodies.

"You know, I did keep it and until a few months ago, still had it," I confess. "I have a picture of it, though." And that, too, is true. I wanted a souvenir of our time together. Because I didn't think it was ever going to happen again. "I can't believe you asked me that. And I can't believe I kept it. You fucker."

He climbs on the bed, rises up on his knees.

I take a deep hit from the bottle of poppers I manage to grab from the nightstand and join him, my back to his chest.

"You're going to take my load." He allows me to spit in my hands and lube up my hole. "And if you remember it takes me a long time to cum."

I do remember. I bend over.

"That's beautiful," he says as he moves in to mount me. When he does, he immediately begins to jackhammer me. He pins me down by putting his hands on my shoulders, then my waist. "Oh yeah," he moans. "That's it."

"Ohhhhh, Daddy."

"You like that, baby? Do ya?" He lies down on top of me, continuing his powerful motions. He puts his mouth to my ear. "Yeah, I forgot how fucking good you are," he breathes. "Close your legs," he says, never breaking his rhythm. "That's it. That's fucking great. Oh, yeah. That feels so fucking good. Oh yeah," he says quietly. Then loudly: "Oh, that feels so fucking good, baby!"

Then he stops. And takes his cock out of me. He looks at my body, out of breath.

"Teeny little ass. God, that ass is so fucking beautiful. Small. So small. Like a fucking boy."

"I'm your boy."

He turns to the mirror to the left.

"Look at yourself."

I do. We look so beautiful together. His larger, muscled form above me. My smaller frame beneath him. He plunges into me and I cry.

"Keep it tight," he grunts through his thrusts.

The power flows back into me again.

"How's that?" I ask him, tensing my muscles, my voice layered with just the slightest coat of cockiness. I bristle with confidence, with knowledge. I have submitted to him yet I am the one in control now. The knowledge of it is bracing. The power of it, liberating.

"Oh that's fuckin' great."

"Is that good, Daddy? You like that, Daddy?"

He raises up into a pushup stance and the pounding grows even more forceful. My previous attitude is fucked right out of me. Now I'm just a whimpering victim and he seems to relish in the exchange of power.

"Oh yeah, that's it, Top."

His pace slows and he leans into my ear again.

"Not a top. *The* top." With his body, he maneuvers both of our forms to the left, so we are looking directly into the wardrobe mirror. "Watch yourself. I want you to watch yourself getting fucked."

I see his face contort into a sly smile, then a sneer. He looks angrily at me in the mirror, empowered by his control over me. All I can do is stare into his reflection. He takes his eyes off my mirror image and looks down at the real me.

"Beg for it."

"Give it to me."

"Work it," he says, powering into the final stage. "Tighten up!"

I know where this will take us. To the end. Part of me is almost relieved. It's almost over. But more, I don't want it to be. It doesn't matter. He'll get his way. I can't refuse him. Not anything. I can't stop him. I clench my muscles. He pounds me harder. Harder. Faster.

"Oh yeah. Oh fuck yeah," he says, panting. Then the louder sounds of him coming to orgasm. Deep, heavy grunts from deep within him, then a roar exploding from his chest. And in me, everything blurs into blackness. I don't know if my eyes are open or closed, all I know is his release inside of me. I can feel my body flood with his cum, hot and blinding. Even after cumming, he keeps thrusting. I open my eyes and look in the mirror. He raises up on his knees, but his cock is still in me, hard and massive. He looks like someone has molded him, cut him from marble. He is magnificent. And he has just been mine.

"Oh yeah," he says, still inside me. He reaches up to the metal bar of the bed. It connects with a *clang!* I know that sound. It's the sound of a ring. The wedding ring on his finger. "Fuck yeah. FUCK yeah!"

I want him to know he hasn't exhausted me.

"Give me a little shove."

He complies. And adds a few extra thrusts to show who is in control of whom.

Then he climbs off of me and comes to stand by the bed, facing the window. The sunlight stripes his face and chest, the slats of the blinds casting the light in an even row of illuminated lines. Shadow, skin. Shadow, skin. The air conditioning unit blasts his naked body with cold air. I stand up to join him and he starts to step aside.

"No. Stay," I say and move in behind him. I take my fingers and touch his shoulders, then lightly cover the span of his muscled back. He moans.

"Oh, that feels so fucking good."

I keep caressing him. I kiss his back. I drop to my knees and begin with his ankles and then travel my fingertips up to his legs, over his calves, his thighs, his buttocks, his stomach, and chest. There isn't an inch of his flesh that I don't touch. Finally, I come up to his neck and move my heads over his head, combing my fingers through his hair. It's so thick. Slightly damp. "Mmmm." Then I kiss him on his ear, he moans a last time, and I release him. He turns to face me.

"Fucking incredible."

He smiles.

He then moves to the bathroom and I stand there, watching him from the bedroom. We make small talk, remark once again on how strange it is to see each other again. I slip on a pair of underwear and lie on the bed while he gets dressed. When he's back into his clothes, I walk him to the door.

"It was great seeing you again," I say. "Thanks for the ride."

"Won't be the last time," he tells me.

Then he gets in his car and drives away.

In just moments, my phone chimes.

I'm a happy man

Thanks, Daddy

That's all I wanted.
I'll be back
A lot

The King is back

Love it
You moan like no other
It made me cum

I have no memory of making any sounds.

You honestly may be the best bottom in this city

And you're The Top
Both t's capped
Have a good one, boomerang

* * *

I still think about that first moment together. It was volcanic. He was the dominant. I was his submissive. He gave the orders and I followed them. It was aggressive, carnal, animalistic, athletic, erotic. It wasn't just a highly charged reunion. It had more weight to it than that. It was a reconnection. Like we were two puzzle pieces who, after trying out hundreds of others that didn't quite fit right, found each other. Yin and yang. Hand and glove. It seems as if we were made for each other, how our bodies responded when brought together. I don't believe in reincarnation or past lives, but he makes me doubt my faithlessness. It seems like we knew each other before this lifetime. This is going to be a perfect arrangement.

And four years later, it still is.

Then I had to fuck things up by falling in love with him.

I don't know, maybe I fell in love with him the moment I saw him. But it doesn't matter. No matter how much I love him, he will never be mine. If the last four years of being with him have taught me anything, they've schooled me on that fact exceedingly well. He'll only be mine in increments, in so many stolen moments. I have no illusions. When he comes, he obliterates me. He is all-consuming and when he's here, that's two hours where I'm not walking through this house like a damaged ghost. Instead of sorrow, there is sensuality. He replaces mental anguish with another kind of pain, one that's easier to live with. And because he chases away the ever-present darkness, I don't just want him, I need him.

I know he'll never leave his husband. Yet since he feels no guilt about our affair, I don't either. But that doesn't mean his partner is never far from my mind. No. I am too resentful of him, too jealous of what he has. And when he has it. There are so many things this relationship gives me. And so much that's taken away.

Never will we wake up in the morning together. He will never spend the night. In fact, I'll never even see him at night, only during the daylight hours, a vampire in reverse. He'll never know my birthday or give me a present. Our friends will never meet. There will never be a random drink or lunch. I will never see the inside of his home, while he will become so at home in mine.

We talk casually after sex but never about anything too deep and the only real revelations that occur are ones of a sexual nature. Still, I ask many questions during these times and he obliges me with cursory answers. Mostly, he's quiet afterward, his mind immediately back at his job the moment the afterglow fades. I learn that he is an interior decorator, a famous one, an in-demand one, and I find it funny because I can't think of a more nelly profession in the world except maybe hairdresser and he is the most masculine man I've ever met.

He is my first thought when I wake up in the morning, he invades most of my waking hours, and his is the last face I see before I fall asleep. Every text I receive from him will send a storm of electric anxiety arcing through my chest and stomach. I will become accustomed to skipped heartbeats and swooning. I vow I won't text him and fail to keep that promise multiple times a day. It is elongated agony to wait for his meager response. Yet other times, he will send a flirty text to me and my entire day will explode into fucking daisies and sunshine. If he doesn't text me back soon after I text him, pathos. And he may not say much when he does respond to my texts, but that doesn't stop me from reading and rereading every message, searching for some hidden meaning. He usually wants to come in the early morning hours and I set my alarm to wake up for his text, the one that starts out "Good morning" and then morphing later into "What's up?" before denouementing to a curt "Hey" in the span of three years. Occasionally he'll break away in the afternoon, but chances are if I haven't heard from him by 4 a.m. he's not coming over today.

He searches the walls in my office for clues about me, but asks me no questions. He lingers over a *Tusk* poster I have framed and it leads me to discover that this is an album by his favorite band. Now I am cursed with every Fleetwood Mac song being a reminder of him, as if I needed any more of those. The only other time we discuss music is when he sends me a video of Terry Nunn's "Somebody's Knocking," that country-pop classic where the singer is debating on whether or not to answer the knock on the door from the devil. *Should I let him in…?* I respond by sending him Garbage's "Empty," one of Shirley Manson's exquisite obsession songs. *I'm so empty/You're all I think about.* He doesn't listen to new music, so he never hears the Garbage song and I make note of it, one more thing on which we are not simpatico. I keep these things close at hand. At times, they sober me. Other times, they console me.

I look for his work via Google and stumble onto so many pictures in the society pages of he and his husband at this party, that benefit, this black tie gala. I wonder about his husband, look at him with such curiosity, and experience a great misunderstanding.

I see images of his interiors and I see that, while he's singularly talented and I appreciate his work, his style of traditional elegance is not mine. But the work is stunning. He has a line of lamps. Every one is exquisite. They illuminate nothing for me.

He tells me his favorite artist is Cy Twombly and I nod, but never tell him I hate Twombly. These are more things we disagree on and I hold onto them as if they're the real reasons we will never be together, why we would never work. Even though he will come into my unlocked house and, on his way to the bedroom, will see me in the kitchen pouring him a drink and say how much he would love to come home to this image every day; me, in a jockstrap, making him a drink before giving him the sex he craves.

He comes over with alternating motives. Sometimes our sex is fierce, carnal, and violent. Other times he wants to make love, have "boyfriend sex," as he calls it. I don't have a preference for either. I'm just glad he's here. Always there is an emphasis on his needs.

He says he wants to be worshipped, as if he has to tell me to do that. He tells me he wants to be treated like the most important man on the planet and I'm dismayed he doesn't realize he already has this title.

Houston has a hurricane and he texts me to check on me and I'm touched, even warmed by this. In the winter he expresses concern over the safety of a space heater I have in my bedroom.

I remember his birthday and send him a card. He never mentions it. But I ask about it, to see if he's received it. He says he has but he doesn't thank me for it. This seems to be a territory too intimate for us to traverse in—birthdays and feelings. Though on holidays he will text me with a wish for a happy one and I'll smile at the acknowledgement that he's thinking about me, though I know it's only a fraction of the times I think about him.

I talk to a friend about him, whining about why I'm so consumed by him. I have told her because she knows of him, she has a friend who is a frequent client. Perhaps one of the clients who fly him to their property on a private jet. He has texted me from the tarmac to say that he'll text me—never a call—when he gets back in town.

"Why *wouldn't* you be thinking about him all the time?" she asks. "He's into you, he's rich, he's talented, he's smart, he's charming, he's successful, he's good looking, he's the best sex you've ever had. *I'm* thinking about him."

I do have another lover, thank God. An architect I've known for years, and until this god showed up, he was the best lover I've ever had. The architect *is* better. But still… One day Kendall asks if he's the only one fucking me, and at first I don't know what to say. Which answer does he want to hear? Which one will turn him on the most? That, yes, I am getting laid by another guy besides him? Does that turn him on to think of someone else fucking me? Or would he prefer that I save myself for him? I decide to tell the truth, that there is someone else. And he immediately claims to be the superior lover. I tell him he's got some competition and our sex that day is delerious. It's like he's fighting over me. My head is dizzy with the thought of that, that I'm prized in this way. It's disorienting that he's a little jealous, if in fact he is. It validates this for me, somehow. It compensates for the lack of information he has about me.

He never sees me out of the confines of this house and I think he likes it like that. Knowing that I am always here, always there for him, always waiting. I fantasize about him booking a hotel room, just so we can have another location to fuck, just so I can see him in another place, to know that he exists in another space, but his schedule is so hectic, brief moments and sudden unions are all we really get. I'm frightened that the truth is he doesn't think I'm worth the effort, or the money.

We do have sex somewhere else, one other time. I am house-sitting near downtown, farther away from his office than my place is. He seems particularly excited about meeting me there. There is a thrill of the new. His lovemaking that day is enthusiastic, even though his departure is quicker than usual because we took longer. The longer we take, the quicker the goodbyes. If he has to fuck and run, he apologizes; but if I would register a complaint, I doubt it would slow his gait. He kisses me quickly on the forehead and I swallow the lump in my throat.

I debate whether or not I am in love or I am obsessed? Probably a little bit of both. Probably a lot of both. I wonder if he has any clue how sincerely lost I am for him. Does he know his power or do I hide it well enough, as unbelievable as that sounds? Or does he read me like a book? Is he as empowered by his hold over me as I am in the hold I have over him? Do I have any hold at all?

To me, he is always Kendall, but in the press he is called "Kenny." A magazine interview with him says this is what his friends call him.

But we are not friends. I make that painfully clear to him when, after an afternoon of sex, he describes us as such.

"You and I are not friends," I reply, laughing. It comes out harsh, mean-sounding. And I don't know if I am saying this because I believe it to be true or if I'm just denying the very thing I want. Or am I just trying to beat him to some punch? That I'm taking away my toy before he can break it. But being friends means something different to him than it does to me, I think. Mine is more involved, more engaging. And his acquaintance level of me seems satisfactory for him. The deep connection we have is sexual. And that's really all he is looking for, so I shouldn't be surprised that he's not looking for more. Even though he told me that, if this worked out, he wanted more, whatever that more was. But to describe us as friends and for me to refute it… I wonder if I've hurt his feelings. I wonder if that is possible.

He hurts my feelings. Every single day. Without knowing it.

And so it goes on, this pain and pleasure, the push/pull of it all. The rapture and the reaping. The damnation and the salvation. I pray one day I'll become numb to it. That I'll be able to just see it for what it is, but I'm not like that. I'll always hunger for more. My want for him is nearly bottomless.

I never cum when we're together. The antidepressants make an erection impossible. And he likes that I don't get hard. He thinks it's hot. More proof I'm meant to be a bottom, he says. His bottom. The very things I hate about myself—my red hair, pale skin, limp cock—these are things that turn him on. How could this not have an effect on me? It's why I crave his company so much. When he's here, he drowns out all the other voices in my head. He's like a priest to all my demons. But also the devil who conjures new ones.

If we were together in a former incarnation, I wonder how it ended. Did it expire slowly? Or did it die suddenly? How long did it take me to recover? Or did I?

Will I?

I'd give anything to know.

I feel him slipping away now. When we first began, he told me I was his new favorite. I wonder who the new favorite is now. He has too great a drive. If he's not seeing me, he's seeing someone else. Probably many. That never bothered me before. Not when I was his favorite.

If I have one lingering regret over this, it would be the fact that we never kiss. I don't know if this is a line he draws in the adultery sand—fucking, fine, but kissing is verboten—or is he just one of those men who doesn't kiss? Strangely, the architect is like that. He claims he's just not a kisser. And so it is with Kendall. I don't begrudge them, though. I used to be like that too. Kissing was too intimate an act. I could do almost anything with another man but that. It was almost like a hooker's code. But now I crave kissing. Especially from him. I asked him. But only once.

"Can I kiss you?"

"Go ahead."

But I felt foolish and feared he wouldn't kiss me back. And I am already too vulnerable with him. I cannot be this bare, not here. So my lips barely brushed his as I came to kiss his hard-edged jaw.

I have told him I loved him though.

It was at his command. It was during the time he was showing me he was a better lover than the architect. Without stopping his rhythm, he stared at me, his eyes flashing mischief. Why, I had no clue.

"Tell me you love me."

I was stunned. So stunned I almost forgot what we were doing.

Do I say it?

Is he telling me to say this because he knows it's true? Is he wanting me to say it because it's just something he wants to hear, that it holds no more weight than any other verbal demand or confession? As I begin to repeat his words, I wonder if it will sound believable? Do I want it to? Or am I afraid for it to?

"I love you," I said, almost in wonder. And in response, he laughed.

"I'm such a sick fuck."

CHRISTIAN'S LAMENT [A COUNTRY & WESTERN SONG]

The Sinner

If I died today would He take me
Or would I go to the other side?
Will I see the gates of Heaven
Or will my flesh be burned alive?

I believe in the news of the Gospels
Though at times I ain't been true
So I claim the grace of Jesus
Because I've been loved by You

I'm a lousy example of what I believe
I've got sin's dirt on my boots
Treacherous heart on my sleeve
They say the devil's highway is full of intent
Forgive me, my Lord. I've got the Christian's lament

Oh if you cause a man to stumble
They say it's a mighty sin
I hope it's one I don't commit
And I don't trip up my friend

No I don't mean to ever doubt You
Though at times my faith might shake
I try to sow goodness and justice
Leave only love in my wake

You've been with me always through good times and bad
You have given me a great joy
And dried my tears when I'm sad
A moment with You is time so well spent
Sins forgiven I've not forgotten, it's the Christian's lament

You know I try in earnest but so many times I fall
But you never forget me
You always answer my call
I've tried to take the high road but I know where I went
I deserve the path of the damned it's called the Christian's lament

Please forgive me, Oh Lord, my Christian's lament

THE SICKNESS SUITE

The Arthritic, the Addict, the Madman

One: The God RA

November 2011

ADV Films, as it was known, is dead. A mighty company of 200 employees with offices in three countries has been whittled down to a surviving 30 with real estate for sale. The boon in anime resulted in a glut of product with more and more titles competing for the fans' attention and dollars. Then the Great Recession hit.

Through some clever, possibly dubious legal maneuvers, the company has been reborn as several—Sentai Filmworks, Seraphim Digital, and other entities. I believe my employer is now Sentai, but I work at Seraphim? It's all very murky and confusing. But the checks don't bounce, so like the rest of the survivors, I put on a brave face and hope the company continues its slow rebound.

The studio slowly grows busier again but, instead of hiring another director and writer to take up the slack, they just pile more onto my plate. And like an idiot, I keep taking what they give me. In this new amalgamation, production timelines are shortened and budgets are slashed. Everything is faster faster, cheaper cheaper. Ten- and twelve-hour work days become commonplace for everyone in production. Mine creep up to sixteen and twenty. The caliber of shows I work on is embarrassing. They're badly animated, poorly plotted, and come with very little fan interest. As I work on them, I can't help but wonder: Who's going to buy this piece of shit?

We've even sunk to dubbing soft-core porn. Of course they don't tell me that. They just let me cast the usual actors in parts where, as the show progresses, their buxom characters' costumes become more and more revealing. A hot-tub scene will pop up in episode 8. There'll be a little lesbian slap-and-tickle in episode 12. There's no time built into the schedule to actually look at the show before recording it. So when the alien-tentacle scene rears its ugly head in episode 15, it's a big surprise.

In Japan, sexual intercourse (and pubic hair) are deemed obscene. Although you can show bare genitalia. But in 1986 an artist by the name of Toshio Maeda thought of a slick way to get around censorship on depictions of sexual intercourse. *Voilà*: tentacle sex. Thus began a boom in sex with aliens, monsters, demons, robots, alien monster demon robots, and on and on—beings or contraptions working with appendages that were penis-*like*. (Fun fact: There's a famous woodcut featuring a woman having sex with two octopi, and all three of them seem to be having a swell time. You might have last seen this image carried by *Mad Men*'s sunglass-wearing Peggy Olson in her now-iconic hall walk in the series' last episode. She carries a framed print of the artwork along with her box of office detritus.) Which is why this show I'm recording features a slimy space octopus, his oozing tendrils reaching out and wrapping around a school girl's legs, searching up under her skirt, and slithering around her torso to come up around her neck, strangling her before inserting itself into the girl's open (screaming or moaning) mouth. If it sounds like rape and it looks like rape…well, folks, it's a duck.

I pitch a holy fit, and once upon a time my protests would have been listened to. But in this new world, in this new company, I'm given an insincere apology and a mealy-mouthed plea to just bite the bullet and record it. To my shame, I go along with this directive.

I apologize profusely to the actresses. I've known these women for years. We see each other socially. They're more than contract workers, they're friends. Because of our friendship, they all (begrudgingly) agree to go along with it. They console themselves by using fake names in the credits, as I've suggested. The fans will still know who's voicing the parts, but at least they won't have their names on it. My name, however, gets slapped on there along with the other poor production saps at the company unfortunate enough to come into contact with the show.

Through the years, the other shows I'm working on are no better. There is one prestige project that comes in. It's another coproduction with a major international studio and a Japanese production house. It was a relationship that began years ago and now they're back with another animation spectacular that is, like all their previous films, gorgeous to look at. The animation is almost painterly in its artistry, photographic in its execution. Years ago when they came in, this movie, like most all the other anime, committed the same anime sins and featured narrative plot holes, rote characterization, and groan-inducing dialogue. It was hard for me to work on the movie and record those lines, so I showed the Korean producer how I approached the work, gave him some of my previous shows, and he jumped at the chance to have me massage the script. Then, it was a good deal all around. They received a script rewrite for free and I got to turn a show I wouldn't have wanted to be associated with into a high-profile project that I could be proud of. And the actors, of course, appreciated the newer, better dialogue.

But now this arrangement is an expected perk, part of the deal. And I'm burned out. Morally, I still bring my A-game because I've got actors and fans relying on me and trusting the company to give them something special, and I don't want to let them down. Pride factors in, as well. After all, my name is going on it. But it means that I work twice as long, twice as hard. From nine in the morning until ten at night, I'm recording—the Japanese director and the Korean producer both in the studio with me, backseat driving. After they leave for their hotel to go to bed, I brew a pot of coffee and settle in to rewrite all the scenes I'll be recording for the next day's recording sessions. I usually finish that around three, four, five in the morning and either go home to grab a power nap and a quick shower or, if I'm really pressed for time, settle for a cat nap on the studio couch and just change my shirt and brush my teeth. This goes on for weeks. But that's not my only problem.

I've been experiencing these sharp stabs of pain, all over my body. There's no rhyme or reason to these attacks, they just happen at random. I'll be sitting at my computer, directing, and suddenly it'll feel like someone's driving a spike into my arm. *Ow!*s *Fuck!*s and *Shit!*s are commonplace. These pains happen so often, I've made a joke about it.

"Someone's got the voodoo doll."

Because that's exactly what it feels like. That someone has a tiny effigy of me in their hand and they're stabbing it with needles.

It's not that bad at first. Just occasionally, barely noticeable. Before I know it, two years have passed and it's become a trademark tic.

But I don't have time to do anything sensible like go to the doctor. I've got a show to record! And then another. And then another. It's a neverending assembly line without breaks in between projects. It's exhausting and demoralizing. And everyone's suffering.

The poor actors. When I started at the company, we recorded fifteen lines an hour. After I got acclimated to the process, I was able to beat that, recording twice as many lines in the same amount of time. Then I designed a new system of recording and the average climbed to fifty an hour. And quality was never sacrificed. It was a win-win.

Now, however, our schedule is so tight, I record upwards of 100, 200 lines an hour. At times it's so bad, I'm just scrolling the script in front of the actors and they're race-reading to keep up with the pace. There are no second takes. Lip flaps barely match. If the line is in the ballpark of their mouth, the engineer throws it down and we move on. All but the plum projects are treated in this way. But as I've said, the plum projects mean *my* workload is extra crunchy.

Meanwhile, my attacks increase in both frequency and intensity. But like the shitty working conditions, I put up with it.

April 2013

We are at a tony little lunch spot, Mona and I. We're having a perfectly fine time, catching up, talking about our kids, bitching about work. Then, suddenly, a stabbing in my right arm. It feels like someone's pierced the muscle with a knife and then taken the whole muscle and is twisting it.

"*Fuck!*" I say, rubbing my arm. "Fuck, that hurt."

"When are you going to go to the doctor?" Mona asks, her voice barely concealing her impatience. "I'm getting sick of it."

"Sick of what?" I drop my fork.

"Sick of you screaming all the time. Something's not right. You've got to see a doctor about this." She takes a sip of her wine. "I'm worried about you."

Hearing someone else comment on something that I've learned to just live with jolts me out of my complacency. She's right. This *isn't* normal. It's been two years since the pains started and they've only gotten worse. Surely my doctor can prescribe some pain medication or something to get rid of it. I realize I've been stupid to have waited this long. But work is all consuming; it's not like I've had copious amounts of time. Still, I tell Mona I'll make an appointment and see my doc.

"You promise?" she asks warily.

"Swear."

It takes me two months to make good on that vow.

July 2013

I have been, for all intents and purposes, a model patient. My doctor only sees me for annual bloodwork. Maybe I get a cold once in three years. But usually everything's rosy. My numbers are good. My good cholesterol is in the stratosphere. My bad cholesterol in the toilet. Kidney functions look good. Liver functions look good, which always surprises me since I used to be a heavy drinker. I have everything except a gold star on my chart.

So it's a little disconcerting when my doctor comes into the examination room and he's scowling at the tablet he carries in his hands. I'm in his office to get the results of some tests he's run. He's *never* been like this. Ever. Which makes me slightly nervous.

"What is it?"

He takes a large inhale and then sighs.

"Well, it's as I thought. Your blood tests came back and you've tested positive for RA."

"RA? What's RA?" I can hear my voice rising a little in pitch.

"Rheumatoid arthritis."

"Aren't I a little young to have arthritis?" This strikes me as ludicrous. I relax immediately. These tests are obviously wrong.

"RA doesn't respect age. It can strike anyone. Usually it's hereditary. Did your grandparents have it?"

"Not that I know of."

"Gnarled hands? Complaining of pain?"

"No, nothing like that. I mean they complained about pain but they were ninety years old. When you're ninety you've got things to complain about. I can't wait to be ninety. I'll be bitching up a storm. You watch."

I laugh. He doesn't. Instead, he rolls his wheeled stool closer to me and sits down.

"Steven, this is serious. There's no cure for RA. It's a chronic pain disease. It can be debilitating. I can't treat you for this. You're going to have to see a specialist. Now I can give you some names of several fine rheumatologists, but you're going to have to be very proactive with this. You can't wait another two years before doing something about it. As you've seen, the symptoms have gotten worse with time. And it's hard to say how much the disease has progressed since you started exhibiting symptoms. You'll have to get X-rays on all your joints to see if there's been any major damage."

"I don't understand. My pain isn't really in my joints. I mean, yeah, my hands are sore a lot and my ankles get a little dicey, but I can *move*." I'm moderating between denial and nervous concern. "Maybe the tests are wrong."

"You can have a false negative but not a false positive. You have an RA factor of 65."

"Is that bad?"

"It's not good. But the number really doesn't mean anything. You can have an RA factor of 10 and have a severe case. You can have a higher number and suffer relatively minor complications."

The news is, to be honest, stunning. I don't know what to say.

"I'm sorry, Steven." He shifts tone. Here comes the inevitable "bright side" of the conversation. "But just because its incurable doesn't necessarily mean you're going to become a severe case. There are medications that can treat the disease. Now it may take some time for you and your doctor to land on a medication that works. With proper care, it's a manageable disease. But don't kid yourself, this is a chronic condition that is only going to get worse."

A few weeks later, I schedule a couple of hours in the recording schedule to take off work and see a rheumatologist.

He's young. He looks like a clean-cut Viking. Slavic features, a randy twinkle in his eye, and a good-old-boy demeanor. For some reason, we really hit it off. I find out he's a staunch Republican and Obama hater, but that's just fuel for our lively political discussions.

Dr. Valicek orders X-rays, more bloodwork, and he feels around on my hands, knuckles, and joints. He's got strong hands. It feels nice to be touched. It makes me realize I haven't been laid in ages. I hate my job.

"That's just it," I explain. "The pain isn't just in my joints. It's all over. In my muscles, too."

"Oh, I'm willing to bet you've got a nice little case of fibromyalgia running tag team with your RA."

"What does that mean?" I'm exasperated. This thing keeps going from bad to worse.

"RA can lead to FMS. There've been some studies that show that chronic pain, from RA or other sources, can lead to FMS by causing changes in the ways the nervous systems perceive and process pain. And I hate to tell ya this, but there's no cure for FMS either. But with some lifestyle changes, it's possible to make the symptoms of the disease easier to live with. Somewhat. But let's not get ahead of ourselves. Come back in two weeks and we'll go over all your results. Until then, don't worry about it. The X-rays may prove different, but it doesn't look like there's been extreme damage to any of the joints in your hands. And we may find a treatment for you right away. There's no reason to be alarmed. There's been a lot of development in treating the disease. I'm sure we'll have good luck."

After two weeks, I return to see him. He tells me there's been no significant joint or bone damage. And the test for the RA factor came back negative.

"That means I don't have it anymore?!" I'm confused. But happy. Hopeful.

"No, it just means that it didn't show up in my tests like it showed up in your others. But with your symptoms, I agree with your doctor's diagnosis. I'd like to start you on a steroid and combine that with another medication. We'll try that for a few months, see how that works. If it doesn't, we'll try something else."

But the pills don't work. I still have the pains. Neither do the next pills. And the pains continue to increase in severity and longevity. The internet tells me these pains are called "flares." And the flares are becoming increasingly harder to deal with, harder to ride out. It's like ever since I found out about the RA, it's been open season. *Now that he knows I'm here, I'll just make myself feel right at home.* The Egyptians worshipped Ra. I know just how that feels. RA is bringing me to my knees.

After months of the prescription drugs having no success, another option presents itself.

I hook up with a guy. Before we get down to business, he asks me if I mind if he gets high. I usually don't play with people who party, but I was lonely and he'd already come over. I told myself it'd be rude to kick him out. When he sparks up, he leans over and offers me a hit. I decline, saying I'll just stick to my drink.

"Come on. You'll feel no pain."

That's all the peer pressure I need.

October 2013

The pain is interfering with my work. I'm short and irritable with people and I'm *never* like that. I try to keep a positive attitude but the flares obliterate that strategy. I'm supposed to make "lifestyle changes." I'm supposed to exercise more, eat better, get more rest, alleviate stress. But work makes this impossible. I'm in a vicious cycle. The pain makes work harder. Work makes managing the disease difficult. Usually I'm able to roll with the punches. But I'm getting tired of being punched all the time. There are certain situations that have me particularly vexed.

Janice, one of the production managers, and I have never gotten along. Usually I take this in stride. With the RA, I have no patience or tolerance for her bullshit. We have words. There's a new receptionist who I feel doesn't like me. Worse, I have a new engineer and when he makes mistakes, instead of owning up to them, he lies. About everything. I've been hard on him, though, I'm sure.

One day, I'm summoned to the president's office. And today the RA is having a field day. I'm grimacing through my sessions. I have no idea what this meeting is about, but it's the last thing I want to deal with. I just want to go back to my studio, finish my work, and go home.

When I enter the conference room, there is the president of the company, along with the company attorney and the poor woman who, ever since the restructuring, has to be both accountant and the HR person.

"Well, this doesn't look good," I say to them as I take a seat on the other end of the conference table. The president seems uncomfortable.

"We've been hearing some…" he says, fishing for words. "We've heard you've been difficult at work," he says.

I run down the list of possible suspects. I think momentarily about explaining each rocky relationship I have. But the flare is messing with my mood and I just feel like it'll be wasted breath. And John loves Janice. So I just tell them this:

"I just tested positive for rheumatoid arthritis. It's a chronic pain disease for which there is no cure. Which means I'm in pain a lot of the time and it's sometimes hard to do my job. So I'm sorry if I haven't always been the ray of sunshine I usually am."

I stare at three blank faces.

Apparently, this is not what they thought they were going to hear.

When they recover, they extend to me their deepest sympathies. John offers his condolences. Everyone is exceedingly sympathetic, as caring as Peace Corps field workers.

Five months later, they're presenting me with a resignation letter they have kindly drafted for me.

I'm confused, angry, and hurt. How could they do this to me after all I've done for them? I refuse to sign it. But if they want to get rid of me so badly, I roll over and suggest we talk severance.

There is no talk of severance.

What?

Now I want to pitch a fit, but the RA is wracking my body and fogging up my head. I feel like I'm about to burst into tears. I feel stabbed in the back. I feel totally betrayed. All I want to do is go home, get high, and make the pain go away. Fuck 'em. I don't need the money. And I can get a job anywhere, RA or not.

I try to storm out, for dramatic effect.

But the limp makes this a feeble attempt.

Two: A Man of Substance

May 2014

I briefly think about getting an attorney and filing a wrongful termination lawsuit. But I tell myself I don't really need the money. And thinking about it only compounds the hurt I feel. Better to just move on. I tell myself I'm better off without them. I tell myself that I didn't like the job anyway. I tell myself everything will be just fine.

The drugs make me believe it all.

June 2014

I am driving down the highway, the same one I would usually take to the studio. But I'm not going to the studio. I'm going shopping. In the middle of the day.

I'm free.

Instead of being trapped in a dark studio on a beautiful day, I'm in my convertible, top down, wind in my (lack of) hair, singing my heart out to the Sam Phillips' "All Over Me," feeling like an Israelite fresh out of Egypt.

It's liberating. No more sleeping on the studio couch at six in the morning before starting another marathon day. No more going on two or less hours of sleep. No more Korean producers behind me sucking up to me to get me to do something that, by all rights, I should be paid extra for. No more ridiculous deadlines. No more pressure! I'm in a fantastic mood. I feel so blessed by God, there are chills all along my body as I sing along.

I'm at the top of my game. I still have RA, but so what? I can get any job I want. And right now, I don't want one.

And today, there is no pain. I've been given some kind of reprieve. But that's how the disease is. Some days, it's slumbering, ignoring me, but lying in wait. Other days, it's attacking with a renewed, perverse vengeance, a desire to make up for lost time. Sometimes it's obvious with its white-tipped spikes of searing agony. I'm unaware of the more subtle punishments the disease metes out—the debilitating fatigue, the loss of appetite, the stiffness after being sedentary too long, the depression. They are all being masked.

Because I'm high as fuck.

September 2014

I have energy, enthusiasm. I'm working on a website I'll unveil on my birthday. It will be the beginning of a grand new business adventure. What will it do? I don't know yet. I'm not worried about it. I'll find out. I'm sure of it.

Some days the pain is so great, all I do is lie in bed and moan.

Other days, you'd think there was nothing wrong with me.

It doesn't matter what day it is, I'm probably high.

November 2014

I am cleaning up from a Halloween party I threw. No, it was more like a Halloween spectacular.

The party was a huge success, though I don't remember much of it. Except that I didn't have time to put my costume together because I was running around putting last-minute touches on the decor. I'd only thought to throw the party a couple of days earlier, you see. So I had a lot to do and almost no time to do it. I even spent the first hour of the party in boxers and a T-shirt, because I didn't have time to change into my costume. I think everyone that came enjoyed themselves.

Still, this is a big cleanup job for one person. But I don't care.

Because I've been high for thirty-six hours straight.

December 2014

In a moment during the holidays, I wonder if I'm relying on drugs too much. But then I get high and tell myself I'm not.

January 2015

I've decided that since I did such an amazing job on the Halloween party and since I decorated the ADV lobby and studios on my own and kicked ass at that too, I'm going to totally redo my living room and kitchen.

For weeks, I concept and sketch until I have an idea and scheme that is just perfect. Then more weeks of running to Home Depot and Lowe's, loading up my convertible with supplies. I must look like the wagon in *The Beverly Hillbillies,* wall-size planks of wood and sheets of drywall sticking high out of the back seat, other supplies stacked on top. I need almost everything since I'm doing the job myself. I have so many supplies and tools.

It never occurs to me that I have no shed for all this stuff.

I'm not concerned with things like that.

February 2015

Stephanie Wittels Wachs' brother has died. They were very close. And I am close to Stephanie. So I am going to go to the funeral.

I hate funerals. I know that nobody *loves* them. But I have a specific revulsion to them. They're all done wrong. We don't talk about death in this country, so none of us know how to really handle it when it (inevitably) shows up. We don't know how to deal with the dying—our euthanasia policies prove that much—so when death finally comes, we lose our shit. We revert to the same gloomy ceremony we've performed for centuries—a black-garbed dirge of an affair. They may claim to be a celebration of someone's life, but the last thing it feels like is a party.

I remember when I was married, my wife's mother died. She wasn't a vain woman, but she took pride in her appearance, always. Her casket was open for her funeral.

I remember going up to pay my respects. I'll never forget seeing her. She looked ghastly, nothing like her living self. I'm not that old, so I haven't gone to very many funeral services, so I don't know if it was just a bad hire or is this usually how embalmed people look. But I remember thinking to myself, *I wouldn't be surprised if she got up right now and demanded to know who made her look like this and beat the shit out of them.*

But I have to go to Harris' funeral. For Stephanie.

This will be the first time I've seen anyone from the studio, really, since I left. I make plans to go with Maggie Flecknoe and Shelley Black. Another actor, David Matranga, says he'll be going, but he doesn't get there early enough to sit with us.

During the funeral, I am overwhelmed. My tears start the second the service starts and they don't stop until it's over. I'm trying to stop crying so hard, I break into a sweat. *Harris is dead. Stephanie won't even return my calls. She must be devastated. Poor Maureen and her husband, I know they're wrecked. Get ahold of yourself. Don't make a spectacle.*

I feel abysmally sad, but overly so. Inappropriately so.

Why am I so sad? Is this what being sober feels like?

No wonder I don't miss it.

Maggie who, besides being a sometime voice actor, is usually a TV journalist on a gossipy morning show goes into mode. She taps me on the shoulder.

"There's Aziz Ansari," she whispers.

Jesus Christ could walk in and it wouldn't stop me from crying.

March 2015

I've moved all the furniture into the middle of the living area. I've already ordered new furniture, so those boxes are stacked up as well. I'm going to repaint the entire space. In fact, I'm going to sand down the texture on the walls until they are museum-smooth. I've even gone on YouTube, studying how to do a professional-caliber Level 5 finish! I've never used a trowel or plaster in my life, but I've somehow determined that this is in my wheelhouse.

I keep tweaking my design. Pages cannot contain my ideas. There are so many.

I'm repainting, I realize. Why not just use the walls?

So I begin scribbling on the walls with a black marker. My mind ablaze with ideas. Brilliant thoughts. Exciting concepts.

Soon the walls are covered with writings, with ramblings, with art, with genius. I work from early in the morning until the next. I do this over and over again. There's not an hour that goes by that I don't write at least a little something on the walls.

This is so exciting.

April 2015

For some reason, I've stopped communicating with everyone. If someone does call or text, I give them a hurried explanation of how busy I am. Then I get right off the phone and go back to…what? What exactly?

The entire house is prepped for renovation, but I never move on to the next phase—actually renovating it. I'm terrified I'm going to fuck it up. In fact, I'm terrified of a lot of things.

I guess that's why I don't go outside anymore.

May 2015

The only time I leave my house is to go to the grocery store. And I do this only at three in the morning, four in the morning. When the store has fewer people in it.

I scurry in, creepily smiling at the African-American security guard, a lovely old woman who always smiles back like I'm an old friend. Likewise, I greet the self-service check-out attendant.

They both always work the graveyard shift, the only time I come in. I don't know what his affliction is, but the attendant definitely has one. I don't know if his legs are uneven, but he walks with a significant limp in his gait. His jaw seems too large for his face. His speech is affected. But I wouldn't inquire about it. That would mean talking to people. I don't talk to people. Not anymore.

I hurry back home with my groceries. I squirrel them away and then return to the living room, a term that seems ludicrous now. But live there, I do. I'm not touching my bedroom, so there's no reason to have a makeshift bed and sleep in the living room, but that's what I do. When I do sleep, that is.

I look at the front of the house, all the windows there.

Each one is covered, boarded up from the inside by giant sheets of plywood or sheets of drywall. Nails in the window frames keep each one secure. Not a shaft of sunlight breaks through during the day. No one can see in. This window treatment seems entirely reasonable to me. Even smart.

I lie down on a blanket, cover myself up with a sheet, and lay my head on a throw pillow. I'm surrounded by walls so graffitied, it looks like a set from *Seven*. Covered furniture fills the room. And the boxes of the new furniture? Oh, they serve a purpose. They've been moved around, forming paths just wide enough for me to get through. They form spaces for me to hide in. Just in case.

I feel safe.

They can't get me in here.

Three: Non Compos Mentis

June 2015

I met Fred more than twenty years ago. Remember the guy from the gay clothing store way back in my advertising days? That's Fred.

We were boyfriends for seven years. And usually when I break up with someone, that's it. Exes turned into friends? I've never been able to do it. Except with Fred. Fred has become more of a life partner in friendship than he was when we were lovers. We are there for each other in the best of times and in the worst of times. I just have to say the word and he comes running. He travels a great deal now for his job, which means we don't get to see each other as often as we once did, as often as we would like.

So when he calls me on a Saturday and tells me he wants to go check out the new Sprouts, a Whole Foods knockoff, he's insistent.

"We haven't seen each other in months. I'll be there to pick you up in two hours," he says before ending the call.

Immediately, I descend into panic.

I'm sane enough to know that he cannot see the inside of my house. Somehow, by long-gone instinct, I know that much. I try to get ready.

It takes me forever. I move in bursts. I'll be standing in the hall one minute, then realize ten minutes have passed. I make an attempt to straighten up the place. Then I realize the futility of that and yell at myself for wasting precious time. I try to go to the shower, but I never make it. I can't even bring myself to look in a mirror. Just picking out my clothes takes me forty minutes. I'm confused, nervous beyond belief.

With the windows boarded up, I can't peer outside. So I stand at the door with it ajar enough for me to look outside with one eye. Just looking at the outside world in the daylight is making me scratch-the-walls anxious. I decide that we'll take my car to the store. That way, I'll have control of the situation, how long I'm out. I can do this.

When I see his SUV pull up behind my car, I rush out of the house and direct him to park in the street.

"I'll drive!" I suggest as happily as I can. I give him a cursory hug and slip into the car as fast as possible. Outside feels *enormous.* Inside the car, I feel a little safer. But I still duck my head low as I crouch down and grip the steering wheel.

In the car on the way, Fred tells me about his travels. I grunt a comment here and there but mostly my concentration is on the road. *Why does everything look this way? Why are the other cars so close? When can I go back home?*

Thankfully, he doesn't ask me any questions. I don't know what I would say. When we arrive at the store, he's so excited about seeing it, he pays little attention to me. This is good. If he looks closely, he might notice.

The walk to the store is an eternity. I keep my head down. Anything could come at me. It could swoop down, unseen, and just...I don't know what *it* is, I don't know what it would do, but it could hurt me. We can't get inside fast enough. My heart is racing by the time we get inside.

I'm barely paying attention to Fred, I'm too busy trying to stay alert for any dangers. To me, the ceiling seems twice as high as it should be. The aisles and layout are too disorienting. I feel like I'm about to cry, I'm so terrified.

"Let's check out the produce!" he says. He's so excited. Fred in a health-food store is like a child in a candy store. Once a bodybuilder, always a bodybuilder. Somehow I manage to spit out:

"You go ahead. I'll take the basket and look over here."

Now I'm left alone.

It is somewhat of a relief. I can't let him see that there's something wrong with me. But now I'm alone among *all these people.* At last I find an aisle that is void of customers. I push the cart into the very middle of the aisle and wait nervously. I look down at the cart. I'm gripping the handle so hard my knuckles are bright white.

My thoughts have all the serenity of an orchestra warming up. The product labels are a dizzying blur. If someone so much as looks down my aisle, I start to panic. I'm frozen here. I can't move.

Eventually Fred finds me. He has a few items in his hands.

"This is great! Don't you love it?"

"I really need to go, Fred. Can we go? I really need to go."

He's a little thrown by the request but he agrees to leave.

As we're in the checkout line, it feels like there is some deadly time limit on me. *I have to get out of this store.* But that means going outside again. *Unprotected.* How far away is the car parked? However far is too far.

Somehow, we are out of the store and I'm practically running to the car. As I walk, I keep pressing the fob to remotely unlock the car doors so I won't have to wait a second to get in. Finally, we're in range and I see the lights flash, signaling that the remote is now within reach and the doors are unlocked. I am in the car with the ignition running before Fred even has his door open. I can't hold it in anymore. I feel everything within me breaking. My hands are shaking. Tears are filling my eyes. Fred gets in and closes the door. I throw the car into reverse.

Fred looks at me with stunned shock. "What's the matter with you?"

I glance at him once, quickly. I'm practically feral. Then my eyes go right back to the front windshield. I don't talk so much as convulse words.

"We have to get out of here. I have to get home. *I have to get home!*"

"Okay, okay. Stop the car. I'll drive," he says, startled.

"Hurry, we have to *hurry!*"

"Come on," he says slowly. "I'll drive. I'll get you home."

I don't leave the car to get to the passenger seat. Instead, I crawl over the stick shift and cower like an animal once I've made it. Fred, like a normal person, walks outside and around.

"Steven," he says softly, "What's the matter, baby?"

I'm hysterical. I'm frustrated he doesn't know how imperative this is. *How could he not know? Can't he sense the danger?* I just keep screaming at him that I have to be home, tell him to drive faster. After that Fred stops asking questions.

As he pulls my car into the driveway, I'm opening my car door while the vehicle is still rolling. I realize the keys to the house are on the ring that's in the ignition. Fred puts the car in Park.

"The keys!" I scream and I reach out and tear them from the steering column. Then I run out of the car straight to the front door, shove the door open leaving the keys inside, and disappear into the house.

Fred enters the house a few seconds later but he stops in the doorway.

He sees the bare walls entirely covered in handwriting and drawings. He sees all the covered furniture pushed to the center of the room. He sees the makeshift bed on the floor. He sees the boarded-up windows. He looks for me behind the boxes.

When he finds me, I'm fetal, crying and swaying back and forth. He takes out his cell phone.

"Mona? We're in trouble."

* * *

The official diagnosis is severe depression, generalized anxiety disorder, mild psychosis, and PTSD. Shorthand: I've had a nervous breakdown. That's what the psychiatrist Fred and Mona have taken me to surmises, anyway.

She asks me: "Steven, are you going to hurt yourself? Do you need to be hospitalized?"

"Please don't call the police! Are you going to call the police?!"

"No, Steven, we're not going to call the police. You haven't done anything wrong. You're just sick. And we need to take care of you. To do that, to best do that, you have to tell me. Do you think you need to be hospitalized for treatment?"

I don't know how I give a convincing answer, but it is decided, after some deliberation, that I will not be admitted. I thank her profusely and keep promising I'll be alright. I also offer a string of apologies to everyone in the room. I can't stop crying.

Mona is given several prescriptions—anti-depressants, anti-anxiety medication, anti-psychotics, sedatives.

Fred and Mona confer with the doctor. I don't hear their conversation. The terror in my head drowns out everything.

Next I'm taken to the Montrose Counseling Center. Fred—like he knows everyone in the gay community—knows the HR director there. Within the hour, I'm in front of the admittance counselor. Her name is Cathy. She's an obese woman with a soft voice and face. I simultaneously want her to embrace me and run away from her. She senses none of this. She is focused, all business. Her sentences are measured and quiet. She talks to me as if she's trying to coax a cat out of a tree.

I'm asked again: "Steven, are you sure you don't need to be hospitalized?"

"No. I'm okay. I'm okay," I somehow manage to say. This is immediately followed by apologies and explanations. "I'm so sorry. I'm so sorry. I won't do it again. I promise I'll be better. Please don't be mad at me."

"No one's mad at you, Steven. We just want to help you. Do you understand? We're only trying to help you. And if you say you don't need to be hospitalized, you're not going to be hospitalized."

I just sit there.

"Do you understand what's going to happen, Steven?"

"No," I say with wild eyes.

She moves closer to me, tells me to look at her. It is hard for me. It is hard for me to look anyone in the eyes.

"We're going to help you, Steven. You've been sick. And you've been sick for some time. We're going to set you up with a therapist and she'll..."

"She?!" It's not that she's female. It's that she's a person. A person could hurt me.

"...or he...will determine how often you need to see her or him and what your treatment plan is going to be. You don't have to *do* any of this. But your friends care a great deal about you, Steven, and they've brought you here to get help. You want to get help, don't you?"

"Yes," I spit.

"Good. You're going to be alright. Everything's going to be okay. There's nothing to be afraid of. Now we're just going to go over some paperwork right now and I'll be asking you a lot of questions. You just answer as best as you can."

"You won't call the police?" I ask in panic.

"No, no, Steven. No one's going to call the police."

"You won't let them get to me? They'll hurt me."

"Who's going to hurt you, Steven? No one's going to hurt you."

"*They* will," I sob. "They will."

"Steven, this is just going to help us determine what kind of care you need. It's going to best help me to find out which therapist on our staff is best suited to help you. Nobody's going to hurt you. You're safe now."

She waits a moment until my crying becomes slightly manageable enough for me to talk.

"Good. Just breathe. Now are you ready?"

"Yes, ma'am," I say. Then I continue crying. "Thank you. Thank you. Thank you so much. I'm so sorry. I'm so sorry. Thank you. Thank you."

Only three other people are told about my condition: my friend Dale and her husband Jim were briefed on the situation after I called Dale in a lunatic state one night; Phillip, who came by my house to see me and discovered my condition; and Shane, a friend who lives in my neighborhood. Dale, Fred, and Mona assign Shane to be the emergency point man in case whatever I am going through can't wait until one of them could get there.

My parents are, of course, told. But Fred explains the situation and they mutually decide it would only upset them to see me like this. Dale tells them about NAMI, the National Alliance on Mental Illness. NAMI works with the mentally ill, but their mission is to educate about, increase awareness of, and de-stigmatize mental illness. NAMI is a revelation for my parents. It gives them the ability to get a handle on things they are otherwise unqualified to deal with. In addition to going to see my therapist twice a week, I attend a NAMI support group once a week.

The "Steven 5" clear my house of all the construction debris and move all the new furniture and decor into storage. Shane volunteers his double-car garage.

I stop taking drugs and within days they are out of my system. To my great shock and relief, it is easy to quit, and even more miraculously, I experience no painful repercussions. No withdrawal, no demonic cravings, no climbing up the walls, nothing. But I'm practically a catatonic zombie so I doubt I would know if I am in withdrawal.

One day, I'm sitting on the sofa, wondering what is wrong with me, why I can't get up. An animated show about depression comes on HBO and for the next hour I listen to Sigourney Weaver explain the disease. As she describes every one of my symptoms that I've been showing for months, I wonder how could I have been so blind as to not see it? How could I have missed it all? How could I not have known?

My therapist, Thomas, is wonderful. He's probably about twenty years younger than I am, which if I was sane, I would probably not be comfortable with. *I've lived so much longer than he has. How is this kid going to help me?* It's a ridiculous mindset. He's a sweet man, slightly reserved at first, and extremely intelligent. He is an admitted sci-fi nerd. He has a husband and a dog. Other than these few things I know, he is an enigma. I don't know if he believes in God (he think it's best if things like that aren't known about your therapist) and I don't yet know how good he is at his job. But he seems to be on his game. For the first couple of weeks, most of our sessions don't get very far because I can't stop crying, so it's not always easy to tell.

I cry all the time now.

I'll be walking through my house, on the way to the kitchen or something, and I'll just stop there in the middle of the hallway. I'll think about my life, the wreck it is—or I can think about nothing at all, actually—and I'll dissolve into wracking sobs, sliding along the wall, sinking to the floor, and remain there until I'm spent. I feel like I've been gutted, completely hollowed out inside. And what has been put inside of me to replace it, some giant black void that just sucks every good thing down into oblivion.

July 2015

At first, venturing outside is still impossible. I'll get to the front door, open it, and freeze. One day, I make it to the car, but just remain in there, screaming like a caged animal and sobbing. I look at my front door and it may as well be miles away. By some miracle, I manage to find the door handle, open the car door, and run inside, shutting the front door tightly behind me.

August 2015

Eventually, I am able to go to therapy on my own. Soon, I can visit the grocery store during the day, though Dale has to go with me. I am still too dicey for crowds. Being outside is still…uncomfortable…for me. That's not the right word. But terrified is too strong. Let's just say I don't like leaving my house but I can do it.

After a shaky start, I settle into a routine and am able to take myself to my appointments, with only the occasional meltdown. Sometimes they are abated by a call to any of the small group of caretakers I have. But most times, I just suffer through them. I can't bring myself to call any of them each time I lose my shit. I'd never be off the phone.

September 2015

I've taken on a whole new set of quirks, tics, and habits. They're all involuntary and I can't stop any of them from happening. They're usually prompted by times of stress. But I feel distressed all the time, so they happen all the time.

They are:

I cave in.

My body physically reacts to these feelings that are too overwhelming for me. My shoulders rise and my head sinks in. My back curves over. If I had scales and was more dexterous, I'd go full armadillo.

I stutter now.

Stuttering is strange. It's like you see the word in your mind, you're heading straight for it. It's like a door. When you get there, you just kind of push it again and again and again and then, finally, it opens. I don't stutter sounds or letters, but whole phrases.

"I can't…I can't…I can't…I can't hear what you're saying."

It happens so quick, I don't notice it for months. Most of the time, I don't give it a second thought. But Fred makes fun of me doing it once and I immediately become angry and defensive.

"Don't make fun of me like that!" I bark. "I can't help it."

"Sorry, I'm sorry," he backpedals. "I didn't know. I thought you were just…I don't know, I'm sorry."

There is The Loop.

I've finally begun the daunting task of finishing my renovation. I'm still terrified I'm going to mess it up, but I keep telling myself, *If you screw it up, you just do it again. Relax. Stop panicking. This isn't life or death.*

I'll be up on the ladder, spreading dry wall compound in sweeping arcs (just like on YouTube!) and something will float into my head. And once it's there, it just keeps playing over and over like a skipping record. It can be a line from a song. Those are just mildly obnoxious.

"Didn't I Didn't I Didn't I hear you cryin'/Didn't I Didn't I Didn't I hear you cryin'/Didn't I Didn't I Didn't I hear you cryin'/Didn't I Didn't I Didn't I hear you cryin'/Didn't I Didn't I Didn't I hear you cryin'/Didn't I Didn't I Didn't I hear you cryin'/Didn't I Didn't I Didn't I hear you cryin'/Didn't I Didn't I Didn't I hear you cryin'/Didn't I Didn't I Didn't I hear you cryin'" and on and on.

See what I mean? Obnoxious, isn't it?

Drives me fucking crazy.

But, oh, when it's a phrase. That's the worst. Usually it's something someone's said to me that I've taken as a criticism. Or a critique I've given myself.

"You're getting on their nerves, Steven. You're getting on their nerves, Steven. You're getting on their nerves, Steven. You're getting on their nerves, Steven. You're getting on their nerves, Steven. You're getting on their nerves, Steven. You're getting on their nerves, Steven. You're getting on their nerves, Steven."

It's torture. It takes me forever to get that loop to stop.

I pace.

I'll be making my way from the living room to the bedroom, and once I'm in the bedroom, I just start pacing the floor, back and forth, back and forth, usually trying to remember what I came in the bedroom for. If I can't remember within a few minutes, confusion, panic, and anxiety begin to build and then I'm just a sobbing mess. Then, sometimes, I don't even remember *why* I'm crying.

The strange inflections.

This happens all the time. "I don't eat much because I'm not hunGRY." See? The emphasis is on the back syllaBLE not the first. "JenNIFfer Lawrence is funny, don't you think?"

It gives my speech a little melody, which is, in its own way, somehow kind of charming. After I do it, I kind of marvel a moment at how odd the words sound when spoken this way. Of all my new tics, this is the one I don't mind very much.

The music.

You know how they always say crazy people hear things? Voices, music. Well, I don't hear anybody talking to me. But the music? I hear that.

It's bizarre how real it sounds. And it's not the same volume as my thoughts, either. It's louder. It physically feels as if it's outside my ear. There is definitely an identifiable tune, but not one that I recognize. And what sounds like singing. But you can't distinguish the voices. It sounds like an invented language, or that it's too far away to make out the words.

The first time I heard it, I actually thought I'd left the TV or the Sonos on. Then I thought someone else had, someone in the neighborhood. I went outside and still heard it. I followed the sound to the backyard and still heard it. I stood there for a long time, listening to it. Then I just accepted it and moved on. It wasn't until it happened a third time that I realized that it was my own mind composing it. It's. *Fucked. Up*. Unnerving, but not unpleasant.

I'm a vampire.

Meaning, I can't see myself in a mirror. Or I *don't* see myself in the mirror. I can go into the bathroom, brush my teeth, even shave (the rare times that I do), and then leave the bathroom. I realize I didn't once look into my own eyes or see myself. I know I must have, surely. But I don't remember doing it. So I have to go back in the bathroom and make sure I didn't leave any shaving cream on my face or have a drool of toothpaste foam at the corner of my mouth.

When I do see myself, I immediately realize why I'm subconsciously avoiding it. I can see the effects of the breakdown on my face. There are bags under my eyes. They're swollen from all the crying. There's no real light to them. They look like the eyes of a dead fish staring up at me from an iced case in the seafood department of my grocery store. I always looked ten years younger than my age. Now I look ten years older.

Epic texting.

We're not talking just a screen full of verbiage. No, we're talking multi-screen balloons. We're talking letters and emails delivered over the phone. Usually they're just a running dialogue of my talking to myself. Sometimes they're just a spilling of words and feelings, me trying to get a handle on some anxiety or fear, and instead of calling and sounding like a maniac, I text it and *look* like a maniac.

Staring.

Doesn't matter what it is, but something will get my attention and I'll just stand there and fixate on it for ten or more minutes. It happened once right after I looked up at this clock I have in my kitchen. In the place of numbers are Vargas girls in bathing suits. I locked onto the woman in the red one-piece and before I knew it the hand that was on the 1 was on the 4.

An aversion to showering.

Before the breakdown, I would shower every morning. If I had to go somewhere that night, I'd shower again before going out. And let me remind you, I was a director and a writer. I sat on my ass all day. It's not like I worked up a sweat. But if I was going out twice, two showers. Now, I'll go three, four—one time six days—without showering. And I get *ripe*. Worse, I'll be like Mary Katherine Gallagher, Molly Shannon's old *Saturday Night Live* character. I'll smell my pits. And I'll be intoxicated by my own rank scent. I'm disgusting.

The humming.

It's a little like the aural equivalent of a child rocking himself to sleep. I find myself humming, either just a note or some nebulous tune, and I don't really realize I'm doing it. Then, when I hear myself, I realize that I'm frightened or anxious and that fear or anxiety has prompted an automatic response. Humming. Like a sprinkler system for a fire. But it's just water pouring down over me, it's not extinguishing any blazes. But I'm not burning either.

October 2015

Little Me.

That's what I've taken to calling him.

When the anxiety overwhelms me. When I panic. When I can't stop crying. That's when Little Me takes over.

I've named "him" like he's another entity because he *feels* like he's another entity.

The best way I can explain it, is it's like I'm watching this child version, or small version of myself. He's frail. Nervous. And he's running around, this way and that, just beside himself with fear. And I'm trying to calm him down. I mean, I'm really *trying*.

"Don't panic. Relax. Get ahold of yourself. There's nothing to be upset about. Calm down," I tell myself/him over and over.

But he doesn't (or can't) listen. Nothing convinces him. He just gets more and more agitated, more and more manic, more and more distressed. And then, in a moment, it changes. I'm not watching him anymore, I *am* him. And then there's nothing I can do. I've gone around the bend. I've crossed some line. And there's no consoling him. Or me. Us.

Then it's all tears and wailing until I just wear myself out. It can go on for what seems like forever. I've never timed them—in that state, there's not much I can do but ride it out—but some have had to have lasted thirty minutes, an hour. They're all-consuming and they're exhausting.

And they never stop.

I know this sounds strange, but objectifying him, identifying this as some crazed person inside of me, someone I really can't control, is comforting, in a way. It explains something that's irrational to me. It helps give it boundaries and defines it. It helps me cope. It detaches me from it, almost. These feelings of terror, of lostness, of doom, of loneliness, of utter despair, of grief, they're all too gigantic and unwieldy. Handling them is like trying to contain an armful of water. They're like massive waves that grow in size until they dwarf me. What begins as a tiny notion or question is, before I know it, some enormous, amorphous intangible I'm trying desperately to control. But I never have a chance. It's too quick, too powerful, too all-consuming.

He is me, but isn't me at the same time.

I'm his creator, but I don't recall making him.

I'm his father, but it's not like I sired him.

I'm his owner, but I have no say over him.

I am he but he doesn't look like me.

We're one person but not the same.

November 2015

I don't know how I'm able to do it, but sometimes I can still operate on a sexual level. I'll be aware enough, sane enough, to seek out sex. And then, when I have sex, it's mind-obliterating, all-consuming. And for two hours I'm out of my head. I'm not myself anymore. I'm just some physical *thing*. Every other part of me has checked out. I'm only this carnal machine designed by evolution and running on autopilot. I am grunting primordial man. I am designed solely for physical sensation. And the entire time, I'm free from the swallowing vortex of feelings I can't control and emotions I have no power over.

I'm not always capable of being in this sensual default.

But the times I am…

It's like it's the only part of my old life I can tap into. It's the only pre-insanity self I can access. When I'm having sex, I have an overwhelming sense of *I remember this.* It's like eating after a fast. *So this is what it tastes like. No wonder I missed it.*

I don't understand it, but it's a short reprieve from the usual mental chaos. So I don't question it.

But I acknowledge its strangeness.

Sexually, I'm a submissive. Somehow, this gives me dominance, for a time, over all my tormentors.

It's one time I'm not outnumbered.

December 2015

I'm in my therapist's office. I am, of course, crying.

"I just don't understand why I still feel this way. I'm not on drugs anymore. But nothing's changed. I'm still so fucked up."

"Steven," my therapist begins with incomprehensible patience. We've gone over this countless times before.

In session, I will be able to break through the confusion and the hurt and the pain and comprehend the subjects we're talking about, even remember revelations I come to. But then I walk out his door and forget everything. Worse, I still cling to the hope that all this will magically go away, that I'll return to "normal," that I'm not fundamentally changed, from the ground up.

"What's your diagnosis again? Generalized anxiety disorder?"

"I don't see what's so general about it. It seems pretty specific to me: I'm anxious about everything," I sniff.

"Severe depression?"

"Yes. I know I'm severely depressed. They got that one right."

"Mild psychosis?"

"Yeah, what is that about? Jesus. What does the major version feel like?" I grab another tissue, blow my nose and fill the Kleenex with snot. My nose is red and my nostrils are chapped from tissues.

He laughs. "PTSD?"

"Yes, that too."

"That's quite a list. Steven, what you've experienced has been trauma. No matter what you continue to tell yourself, your brain interpreted these events as trauma. You were diagnosed with rheumatoid arthritis. The studio betrayed you and you lost your career. You were self-medicating. For God's sake, Steven, just one of those is enough to psychologically derail a person. And you experienced all three at the same time."

"When you put it like that, it sounds bad."

"It *was* bad. It *is* bad. Steven, again: this is an illness. It's just like if you broke your leg or you had cancer."

"What? The RA?"

"The RA, the mental illness, all of it. But the good news is that your disease…diseases… have been diagnosed. You are now, as we say, in recovery. But you've got to stop thinking that this is all just going to stop tomorrow and things are going to go back to the way they were. It's delaying your healing. You're disabled now. You have to face facts. You were fired from a nearly twenty-year career."

"Technically, I quit."

"Yes, technically you quit. But at the heart of the matter is that you told them you were sick, and then five months later they had your resignation letter ready. You feel betrayed. At a core level. It's why you're afraid of people, afraid to go outside. It's why you're so terrified of this mysterious *they* that you speak of. *They* are just a personification, nebulous though it may be, of the hurt feelings you have because of the work situation. You were deeply hurt. Your brain remembers that. Now your brain is on heightened alert, thinking anyone could do the same. Sure, the relief of not having that job anymore was refreshing. We know the drugs helped. But they were just covering your true feelings. You know that wasn't going to last forever. What about your plan again?"

"I was just going to get in my car and drive."

"Where?"

"Nowhere."

"What was going to happen when you arrived at this 'nowhere?'"

I swallow hard. I feel like I'm an old man in a child's body.

"I never got that far. But I always saw desert. I would drive until I ran out of gas in the desert."

"And then what?"

"Then, just...walk. Till I passed out. Till I..." I look out his office window.

"Steven, that's a suicide plan. It doesn't involve a gun or pills but in the back of your mind, you had a suicide plan."

"No," I tell him. "That's not me."

"That's *not* you. That's what I'm trying to tell you. This isn't you. *You've* changed. Depression is caused by several factors. Faulty mood regulation by the brain, there's genetic vulnerability, stressful life events, medications, medical problems. The only one you're missing is genetics."

"That is true. I'm the first person in the family to go crazy."

He gives me a slight scowl. Thomas hates it when I use the word "crazy."

"Don't say that word."

"Why not? It's accurate."

"Steven."

"Okay, okay, I'll quit saying it. But I can't quit thinking it."

"We'll tackle that problem another time," he says. "The amygdala is activated when a person recalls emotionally charged memories, such as being attacked, having someone close to you die, even losing a career. Activity is higher when a person is clinically depressed. This increased activity continues even after recovery from depression."

"Well, that's great."

"Your thalamus is affected. It's the part of your brain that links sensory input to pleasant and unpleasant feelings. The hippocampus registers fear. It's literally smaller in depressed people. We're talking about complex systems here. And you keep splitting."

Splitting is, according to the dictionary, the failure in a person's thinking to bring together the dichotomy of both positive and negative qualities of the self and others into a cohesive, realistic whole. It is a common defense mechanism. It's a close cousin to black-and-white thinking, a pattern I cannot seem to break.

"Why do I keep looking for one answer as to why all this happened?" Therapy is so frustrating. Helpful, yes. I think it should be mandatory for everybody. But it's so aggravating. It's like I'm lost in this thick forest. Thomas is in the forest, too, but I can't see him. I do hear his questions, however, and they lead me to certain discoveries along a trail. Signposts. They lead me to a path that, one day, hopefully, will eventually lead me out of here. But now? Now it's just a winding, torturous road famous for having blind corners. "Because I think if I find that one, then I'll somehow be able to fix it. And all this will go back to normal."

"What is normal?"

"Normal is…how I was?"

"Before you had RA."

"Yes."

"Before mental illness."

"See, that makes me sound like…like I'm crazy. That I'm never going to get better."

"To you, better is a return to what it was. That's not going to happen. You're going to have to live anew. You're going to have to live your life with the acknowledgment that you have RA. And all that that realization comes with. That you're going to experience malaise. That you're going to have flares. That you'll have to deal with pain. That you can't burn the candle at both ends anymore. Those days are gone. Mourn that. Then accept it. Accept that you have RA. Accept that you suffer from depression."

"I don't want to accept it. I don't know *how* to accept it."

"And that's going to slow your recovery," he says quietly. "It will take time. Just like you say you can't stop running at a fast pace. You're still in..."

"Production mode."

"Production mode. You still act as though there's some crushing deadline you have to meet. You say that even folding your laundry, you're speeding through it. And stressed by it."

I turn back to staring out the window. A bird flies by. I wish I was one of them. I feel like I *was* one of them. A tear slides down my cheek. I can feel the dampness trailing on my skin. It feels like someone's drawing on my face.

"I'm so sick of being so sad," I tell him. "It's this enormous... *thing* I can't get away from. Because it's not outside of me. It's in me. It *is* me. In me/is me, in me/is me. It's this great blackness and everything has been sucked into it. Everything I used to be but I'm not anymore. It's so far in there, I can't even see it anymore. It feels like...I get glimpses...of this guy, you know? And he looks so much like me. But he acts differently. He's confident. He's funny. He talks to people. He laughs. And that's nothing like me anymore. I can *feel* it. I'm not like that anymore. I look at him and I want to be him so bad. But it feels like I can't." I pause, sniff. More liquid lines are drawn on my skin.

"Just because you've changed, just because these things have happened to you...the RA...the trauma...the depression...doesn't mean you can't experience positive feelings again. What's the one thing that stops your crying…what do you call them? Crying jags?"

"Yeah. I don't know if it's a word I made up or not. Or maybe I heard it somewhere."

"Let's look it up."

Whenever something comes up that might need clarification, illustration, or research, Thomas starts typing on the iPad that's permanently on his lap. Mostly, he uses it to take notes. I'd kill to know what he writes down.

"Here it is. Crying jags. 'When you can't stop crying for a long time no matter how hard you try.'"

"That's it alright."

"It's in the Urban Dictionary."

This makes me smile.

"I'm in there."

"Where?"

"The Urban Dictionary."

"Really? How so?"

"Fosterize."

He types on the keys.

"Ah! Here it is." He's quiet a moment while he reads the entry.

"Yeah, I don't agree with the definition exactly," I tell him. "But I think it's funny that I'm in there. It's actually meant as a critique of the way I work…the way I *worked*…but I didn't take it that way. I thought it was cool, to be honest."

"What do you think now?"

"What do you mean?"

"You said you thought it was cool. Don't you still think it's cool?"

I think about this a moment.

"I guess," I admit. "It's like it all ended so badly, I can't look back on any of those years and see them for the good they were.

I had some really good times there. I was really good. I did some great work there."

"I think that's just temporary. I think, after time…when the hurt starts to ebb…you'll be able to look back at your career and not feel pain. You'll be able to look at it and see it for what it was: a fulfilling, fruitful, exciting time in your life. It's not where you are now, but you experienced it." He pauses. They're funny, these pauses. I can't tell if he's thinking about me or planning his next question. Or is he doing his laundry? I don't know. "Let me ask you something. If they called you tomorrow and wanted you to come back, would you go?"

This strikes me as ludicrous.

"They wouldn't do that."

"What if they did?"

"No," I say. "I wouldn't."

"Why not?"

"The place was a punishment in those last years. That job was killing me."

"Literally. It was. How long do you think you would have been able to keep up a pace where your workday was fifteen, twenty hours?"

"With or without drugs?"

"Either."

"Oh, I wouldn't have lasted…well, I guess I didn't last. I broke."

"*Yes.* You *broke*," he says this quickly. His eyes flash and he smiles. I feel like I've been given a reward somehow. Like a dog gets a treat. "And what's happening now?"

"I'm…" I think for a moment. There's something in the forest. "I'm being fixed?"

"You're being fixed," he says. "And what happens after you get fixed?"

"I can get back on the road again?"

"Yes. Yes, you can."

He's quiet again, letting this sink in. But the thoughts are too confusing for me. Everything is piling up on each other. I can't focus. He clears things up for me.

"Is the car that gets back on the road the same car?"

"Well, yeah."

"But it's changed. It has new parts. Maybe a whole new engine. Maybe it had to be rebuilt totally from scratch. Is it the same car? Or is it a new car?"

"I don't know."

"Why can't it be both?"

The answer stuns me. Again, this wasn't a possibility I considered. I speak only in breaths, barely audible.

"Why can't it be both?" I repeat after him. I smile. "Yeah. Why can't it be both?"

January 2016

I've been like this for six months now.

March 2016

I break down in the hall again today. The depression is so invasive, so all-encompassing; it's like an ailment I can feel, like an injury. From the depths of despair, I just scream, asking God why won't He show some mercy and just kill me? *Why won't You just kill me?*

July 2016

I rediscovered prayer today. It was like a sudden awakening. I realized in my soul and felt it in my whole body: I haven't prayed in years.

Maybe I was subconsciously too resentful. Maybe I blamed God. Maybe I was just so crazy it never occurred to me. But I prayed today for the first time in...at least two years, excluding random screaming sessions at the general cosmos.

And it felt...good. It felt *good*. And not like I was just praying to brass heavens. It really felt like Someone was listening. For once.

January 2017

It seems like every month, I'm spending half my time at doctors' offices or the pharmacy. There's the psychologist, the psychiatrist, the rheumatologist, a new general practitioner, and for a lifetime arrhythmia condition that—thanks to the all the chaos—has been acting up, there's the cardiologist.

Is this what my life is going to be like from now on?

March 2017

By some miracle, the new drugs my rheumatologist prescribed me four months ago are working. I haven't had a debilitating attack in two months. I still have some effects from the disease, but as far as the pain goes, it's been limited to the rare flare.

It is one of the rare bright lights in what is a daily, dark existence.

July 2017

More than two years of this now. *Two years*.

January 2018

It's been fifteen days since I last cried. This is a record.

Therapy remains a lifeline, and slowly, I discover things about myself. My flawed ways of thinking, mostly. I'm still so dense about it, though. I take a notebook to every session and write notes or revelations I've come to. Then I leave the office and never open the stupid book until the next session. I'm so sick of going over the same things. Over and over. I'm an idiot.

This year, I've actually met people for dinner out. I can leave the house whenever I want. I still don't do it a lot, but I can if I choose. I can't remember my last public breakdown. I've even driven to the Hill Country house where my parents live, a three-hour drive away. So many other little accomplishments.

It's actually happening.

I'm getting better.

March 2018

I've gone a whole month without crying!

April 2018

I'm going to give a panel at A-Kon, the nation's second largest anime convention. More than 35,000 people attend this con. I never attended anime conventions when I was in the industry. I was more than willing to have the actors get all the limelight. But ten years later, *Ghost Stories* has proved to be a cult hit, garnering millions of views and fans on YouTube. The thousands of comments written have been a lifesaver to me. They've helped me look back on my career and see it for the good it was—not solely for the hell that the last years were. I'd like to give something back to the fans who gave me such a successful career in the first place. So I'm doing a presentation that hits the highlights in my career, one that'll take the audience behind the scenes of some of their favorite anime shows. I feel like this is some major test for me. To see if I can do it. I veer between *I can do this kinda thing in my sleep!* to *What the fuck are you thinking?* I'm glad there's a signed contract. It keeps me from backing out.

May 2018

I have a car accident. Cars suddenly stop on the highway and I hit my brakes, but still plow into the back of the one in front of me.

This is monumental for one reason: It happens and I *handle* it. No breakdown, no hysteria. I just *handle* it.

June 2018

The con appearance goes really well. I'm surprised as hell, but I can actually draw a crowd. The fancy, gorgeous Mac Keynote presentation I give goes off without a hitch, and maybe even more importantly, I have a great time doing it. Fred's come with me for emotional support and I doubt I would be able to do it without him. But the fact of the matter is, I'm doing it. It's nice to meet the fans and thank them personally for supporting me all those years. They're all incredibly nice people and it makes me regret being a snob all those years and not going to cons more often.

Three years ago, this would have been impossible. Two years ago, it would have been impossible.

Now? It's a breeze.

I've come such a long way in three years.

August 2018

I can't remember the last time Little Me showed up. Or the last time I had a crying jag.

I can't say I feel like my old self again, though. I'm afraid to admit it, but that doesn't seem like it will ever be possible again.

That person is gone. He's been replaced by someone else. Either that or the previous Me has been so irrevocably altered by everything that's happened, he may as well be an entirely different person. It's not like he's recognizable to me.

I have a revelation in therapy that I haven't really mourned the Old Me. I haven't come to the reckoning that he's gone forever. It's like I still hold out the chance that all of this is still going to disappear one day. It seems more and more unlikely. The evidence seems to stack up against it. But I can't let go of what once was. My life is nothing like it was before. That life is gone. In some ways, speaking at the anime convention helped me see that. But it's not just my anime life that's gone, it's the decades before that. The person—or persons—who lived that life is gone, gone, gone. I need to make a new life.

I just don't know how to go about doing that.

January 2019

"Think of this as a kind of graduation. A marker on how far you've come." This is Thomas. He's trying to spin his new promotion as something positive for me.

"You're leaving me," I tell him flatly. "Don't try to make this seem like it's some kind of a benefit."

"Nobody's supposed to be in therapy forever."

"I thought I was going to be seeing you till the day I died. Now you're blowing me off. Ditching me. Abandoning me." I can tell by his face, he doesn't know if I'm kidding or not. "I'm just fucking with you." I force a smile. The longer it stays on my face, the more natural the smile becomes. "I'm really happy for you. And your new office is nice. Bigger than your last one."

"Really? Thank you, Steven."

"I don't like it. But it's bigger."

"Thank you, Steven," he repeats himself, this time with a layer of sarcasm.

"Again: kidding."

"Have you made a decision? Do we close your case file or do I refer you to another therapist?"

"I've been really thinking hard about this and…" I'm nervous to say it. I'm afraid that if I do, all its truth will evaporate like rain on a hot July sidewalk. "I think I'm going to be okay. I'm not saying it's going to be easy. You've been with me for—Jesus!—four years now?"

"Almost four years."

"God, that seems like a thousand lifetimes ago."

"You've come a long way. Do you remember how you were when you first started coming to these sessions?"

"No, thankfully."

"For the first several weeks, you wouldn't even sit in the chair. You'd sit on the floor, right there. Well, right there in the other office."

"Oh my God, I couldn't stop crying."

"You cried a lot."

"I cried for three years straight. You can tell by looking at my face. Before and after pictures, you'd think they were taken thirty years apart. It's tragic."

"So what things are you most proud of yourself for?"

"It's you. You saved me. You really did."

"No," he says firmly. "You did all the work, Steven. That was all you. It wasn't an easy crawl, but you did it. You climbed out of it."

"I was a long way down, wasn't I?

"You had some issues."

"Ha! That's a nice way of putting it."

"So tell me."

I think a moment. It's hard to come up with just one thing. So many things have changed.

"Well, there's the obvious. I'm not agoraphobic anymore. People don't scare me anymore. I don't think everyone's going to hurt me. I'm getting out more. I'm writing again."

"I just saw you had that interview in *Houstonia*."

"Yeah, yeah. That was something I didn't see coming. I had a really nice lunch with the editor. And they're open to me doing something for them again. I'm working again with *OutSmart* occasionally. I'm in a good position. I can afford to choose the work I want, and if I don't want to do something, I don't have to."

"And Kendall?"

"That has faded. Like the mental illness faded. But at the time, he was something I needed. He was a lifeline in a lot of ways. He came into my orbit when I was in a bad place."

"But you've seen how that relationship was ultimately..."

"Toxic, yes. But I can't help it. I'll always have a soft spot in my heart for him."

"In general, how do you feel?"

"I'm proud of myself," I say quietly. "I'm really proud of myself. I've come a long way. Still struggle with that black-and-white thinking, though. You know my living room is..."

"Black and white, yes. You know, I would think it would be a reminder to you. Do you ever stand right in the middle of it, between the black and the white and say to yourself, 'This is exactly where I need to be?' "

"No, but I should do that," I nod. It is a good idea.

Neither of us say anything for a long moment.

"I'm really going to miss you, Thomas. I'll never be able to thank you for what you did for me."

"No. You did it all."

"You can't take a compliment can you? You know, now that I'm leaving you, I could give you a thank-you gift finally."

"Nope. I still couldn't accept it."

"I'd just drop in at your door and run. You'd have to take it. Besides, who'd care?"

"It's against policy."

"It's stupid."

Again, silence.

"Well, shall we get your file closed?"

He stands up to walk from the little living room in one corner of his office to his desk a few feet away. It's strange watching him walk away. It makes me wonder how I'll feel when I'm really outside of here. When I realize I won't be seeing him anymore, that for the first time in four years I won't have his counsel. It'll be just me in the forest. I won't hear his prompts, his questions, his hints, his encouragements.

"Maybe," I start. "I…you should kick me to someone just in case."

He turns around.

"You think so?"

I think about it a minute.

"Yeah, I think it might be a good idea. Just in case I freak out when it hits me that I'm really not going to be seeing you anymore. Maybe I'll need her just to deal with our separation and that's all I'll need her for."

"Would you prefer a woman?"

"No, no. I just said her. I don't know why I said her."

He seems to appraise me. Then he nods and smiles.

"Alright. I'll look and see who has room in their appointment book for you…"

"You can suggest someone, right?"

"Yes. And the Center will call you in a couple of weeks to set up your first appointment with…whoever."

"Sure," I sigh. "Sounds like a plan."

In the end, in the awkwardness of saying goodbye, a hug feels wildly inappropriate and a handshake feels too formal. So, instead, we just regard each other. I smile. He smiles. I nod. He nods.

"You know if this was just a year ago, I would *not* be handling this well."

"I think you're going to handle this just fine."

"Thanks for that. I appreciate it."

"You're welcome."

"Goodbye, Thomas."

"Good luck, Steven."

I meet with my new therapist, Ellie, for just a few sessions. Seems I'm handling life without Thomas quite well. The few times I come to the Center to see Ellie, I never catch sight of Thomas in the hallways. He'll become another part of the nightmare that continues to fade away every day.

March 2019

Will anyone notice that the walls are museum-smooth? That they've been stripped down practically to the drywall and layered and sanded, layered and sanded until it's attained a Level 5 finish? Probably not. I do. Down to the most minute detail, the room came out just as I'd envisioned it. I might have designed it when I was mad, but it makes me very happy.

If you come in the front door, the first thing you notice is the color palette. Or lack of it, rather. The entire space is white—from the Level 5 walls to the doorways that have been covered with white draperies, it's one seamless white box. There's the white Corbusier couch with its white fur and white metallic pillows. On the wall behind the sofa are three large white sculptural panels. Before it, a white table with a white sculpture of what looks like a sci-fi seashell and small tower made of crystal. Another wall is adorned with animal heads—elephant, horse, deer, lion, gazelle, etc.—each of them in white. Below them sits an upholstered white bench inlaid with crystal buttons. There's a white leather chair with matching foot stool. Even the Sonos speaker is white. All the furniture sit on one of two rugs. On the left, a white rug with black filigree. To the right, a black rug with white filigree. It's the only thing grounding the room, keeping it from visually floating away. It's striking, this all-white world.

And before you ask; no, I never drink red wine in here.

But then you come inside the room and, if you turn around, the space is entirely different, a chromatic opposite.

Here, the walls are painted pitch black. There's a black entertainment center with black objets d'art and a large black flatscreen and sound system. On the walls, black art pieces, a black candelabra with black candles, and a black frame with a single black rose floating in the middle of it. There is a black sofa and, standing behind it, a slender, futuristic black mannequin, her shape barely distinguishable against the black wall. She almost looks like a shadow. On the floor is a black bust of a horse with a flowing black mane. Hidden in plain sight is another Sonos speaker in, of course, black.

Before I designed it, I thought it might get old fast, having an all-white and all-black room. But it turns out having a space with a split personality is endlessly entertaining. The more you stare, the more you see. Objects seem to vanish and reappear depending on where you stand. Most days, I sit in limbo, looking out to a black room. Sometimes, I'll sit on the black couch and watch the white. It's a bit like living in a painting.

I'm sitting in the exact middle of the room, in between the black and white sides.

Now we are back at the point where we started this little adventure.

You, me, the bowl filled with my selves.

Now that bowl is empty, a pile of unfolded slips of paper to the right on the carpet.

And it's time to find out who's left.

I close my eyes and start breathing deeply.

In, out... In, out...

LE VRAI MOI

The Real Me

Generally, human thought can be categorized by two models: the verbal and the visual. If you're thinking about meeting your friends for happy hour and picturing yourself with a nice cold drink in your hand, you're probably thinking visually. If you're wondering what you're going to say when you're at that happy hour, you're likely thinking in words and sentences, creating inner speech—verbal thinking. But are they separate? Can you utilize one without the other springing up?

A Harvard study found that even when people were prompted to use verbal thinking, they created visual images to accompany their inner speech, suggesting that visual thinking is deeply ingrained in the brain. The theory goes that we're primarily visual thinkers. Only through evolution have we become verbal thinkers.

If you read a card that says, "a castle in the sky," do you picture a castle sitting on top of a cloud? Or do you just think of it in verbal terms because that's the way the thought was first introduced to you? Is that even possible?

When I describe my selves, I'm using verbal thinking. I don't conjure up an image for each self. They're not standing there in some kind of uniform or costume. They're more like a spirit, something ethereal. Tangible, yes. Visible, no. Likewise, when I'm describing certain thoughts, I'm verbally translating an "unseen" image. But sometimes those thoughts are given a visual representation. When I say I feel uncomfortable, I might picture a stiff wooden chair. I don't "see" myself on a stiff wooden chair, but this is the visual representation that my brain assigns it. Follow?

Meditation doesn't have a whole lot of visual appeal. You're just drifting—or cruising or flying or floating—in nothingness. (I'm assuming you "see" [or, rather, don't "see"] the same thing I do, which is blackness.)

The concept of meditation had always eluded me. When I was in therapy, meditation was suggested as a way to deal with my bouts of anxiety, to prevent emotional meltdowns. But I was never able to get a handle on myself enough *to* meditate. The deeper I came into my recovery, I tried to meditate, but the endeavor always left me frustrated. I would meditate but I couldn't quiet my mind and I'd get frustrated and just quit.

Then I happened upon Dan Harris' terrific book *10% Happier*. In it, Harris demystified meditation for me. It was the first time I had had someone explain the practice to me in simple terms that a moron like me could understand:

Focus on your breathing.

That's it. That's all you have to do.

Harris explains that our "monkey mind," as the Buddhists so brilliantly named it, is constantly bouncing around. Thoughts are always popping up as you meditate. Your job is surprisingly simple. You are to simply acknowledge the thought and move on. *Yes, I see you, Punisher, and, no, I'm not listening to you now.* Or *Yes, I see that I'm being reminded that I have things to do, I'll get to you later, thanks for coming by.* And so on. Check the thought for what it is, then let it pass. Go back to concentrating on your breathing.

It takes practice. And if your monkey mind is anything like mine, it does everything but throw feces. The fucking monkey never stops. But after a while, you are somehow able to reach a detente with the monkey. You come to a place, a peace, where you're able to just...be. Which is where I am now, sitting in the middle of my black-and-white room, empty bowl in my hand, eyes closed, and breathing.

In, out... In, out...

Now that I've taken all my selves out of the bowl and set them aside, it's like the club has emptied. (This is all verbal thinking. I'm not picturing some empty night club.) The crowd is gone. Just like the bowl is empty, so is my mind. This space is now a void. It is my hope that, out of this emptiness, my True Self will reveal itself to me.

I just sit inside my body, letting my interior "hollow out."

If I concentrate—on my weight, on my skin, my sense of touch—I can tell that, yes, I am sitting on a rug and that, yes, there is something in my hands. But being in a state of meditation, concentrating only on my breathing, I start to lose touch with my body. And to some extent, my senses. There is no taste in my mouth. I hear nothing but the drone of ambient noise. I see nothing but blackness. There is no aroma to smell. After a while, if I don't move, I can't really feel that I'm touching anything, that I'm sitting on the rug or that there's a glass bowl in my hands. My outer senses are powered down and I'm focusing on my *inner* senses. I'm looking for something in a vast nothingness. Sure, occasionally my monkey mind will bring up a distracting thought, but just as I've been taught, I don't berate myself for it, I just gently ignore it, or push it away, and get back to my meditative state. My only task is to stay the course and be open to whatever feeling or sensation or notion that may come to me out of the darkness.

I alternate between two tactics: either I simply relax and try to be as receptive as possible or I make a more conscious effort to actively seek.

When I take the passive route, I'm just hovering, waiting. I "open up my mind" as far as I can. I lose focus. I sort of sit back and wait for something to show itself to me.

Then there is the more active approach. It's like I send out waves, like sonar. Hopefully, these waves will bounce off and I'll discover it that way. I'm hoping that "something" will be my inner self, my true self, the one that is so frustratingly hidden from view.

Setting aside my other selves was relatively easy to do, and to my surprise, they don't creep back and try to assert some kind of authority. Maybe having this physical representation worked out better than I thought it would. Good, then. So far, everything's going according to plan.

All the while, I sit and I breathe.

In, out... In, out...

Usually it's boring as fuck.

But somehow, this time, it isn't. I am not a patient prayer or model meditator. Most times the prominent visual image—that is represented by verbal thinking—is that of a racing clock. Again, I don't see a clock floating there. But I do feel the need to hurry and wrap it up and get back to *doing* something. When you're doing something, you see a measure of your progress. With meditation, it's all just vague moments and endless waiting. But surprisingly, I'm neither impatient nor frustrated. I feel, at least as best as I can describe it, quite peaceful. What I'm seeking will be revealed. For some strange reason, I trust that. Though my mind is a maze that is frustrating to explore and my soul is a vast expanse of question and mystery, I know the real me is somewhere out there in the void. What is formless will take form. What is difficult to see will be made clear.

In, out... In, out...

Out of the blue, my body suddenly demands attention.

My mouth is dry. I'm thirsty.

There's a spot on my leg. It begs to be itched.

I tell myself water will come soon enough. I ignore the desire to scratch. I keep breathing.

In, out… In, out…

Moments pass by. A thought pops up. "How long is this going to take?" *It takes as long as it takes, now leave me be.*

More moments creep by.

And then…slowly, ever so slowly, I start to feel something.

An awareness begins to dawn on me. It's subtle at first, just an inkling. I don't startle. I just keep breathing and relax about it, letting the feeling come to me.

And it *does.*

It feels like some kind of low-range anxiety. *I'm* not anxious. It's more like I sense the presence of anxiety. As if someone else is in my head with me and I'm picking up on what they're feeling. I can feel a quivering all around me. Again, I'm not quivering. But I get the sensation that something is.

It makes me uncomfortable, uneasy. The more I sit with it, the more it takes on form. *What does it feel like?*

It feels like fear.

When I name it as such, a surge of adrenaline flushes through my heart and chest. It's as if my body's reacting with recognition. *Yes, that's right.* The feeling has been identified and it asserts its power. I just keep riding it out. *What am I afraid of?*

I can't say. It's just…a fearfulness. Its presence is undeniable. I stay with it. I don't run from it. I let it take over me as best I can. I try to discover its origin. Again, I maintain my breathing.

In, out… In, out…

Suddenly, I'm overwhelmed by a sensation. One of *smallness*. It's like I'm outside of myself watching myself. And everything about me is shrinking. I can feel my body. It hasn't changed posture, but I can't help but feel my shoulders are slumping, that my body is turning in on itself. It's like a turtle retreating into his shell, a defense. It's like I'm trying to disappear from something. Hide. Again, I'm not doing these things. They're feelings. Impressions.

I concentrate. I send my thoughts outward, like feelers. What is this perceived aggression? What am I feeling I need to defend myself against?

Everything.

Yes. Everything. It's like when I was crazy, just not to the same mad extreme. Whatever is out there, it means to do me harm.

I begin to sense this small, bowed thing. Verbally, not visually. It's meek. Tentative. Nervous. I get the distinct feeling of powerlessness, of apprehension. Verbal thinking continues. Hansel and Gretel lost in the forest. *Yes, that fits.* An insect under a microscope. *Yes.* The accused at a trial. *Yes, that too.* Someone who's guilty. Then, just as the Harvard study showed, my brain can't limit itself to the one mode and there are accompanying visuals.

These images are starting to make me anxious. I tell myself to relax. Stay with it.

Immediately, I'm aware of my body and I wonder how long I've been sitting like this. I think of how much it's going to hurt when I unfold my legs. *Okay, that's later. Just concentrate on the now.* And I gently push that thought away.

Everything in me says to panic, but I don't. I sit in the feeling, resign myself to it. But I move to a more active participation.

Then, very quickly, a visual comes to mind.

I'm a terrible draftsman, but I make a rudimentary sketch of what I "see." I can't draw very well in real life, so I don't "draw" the image very well in my mind.

It's a cartoon, really. All large eyes, fearful. Tiny nose. Just a small thin line for a mouth. Shoulders are hunched, and arms are folded in across the chest and belly. He's standing on two tiny legs and two miniature feet. He's drawn in a downward perspective.

Larger at the top than at the bottom, as if viewed through the opposite end of a telescope.

Vulnerable.

Yes, that's what it is. *Defenseless.*

I stare at what my mind has conjured up.

Is this it?

Is this who I really am?

Then I realize: *I know who this is.* I know this person very well.

Little Me.

* * *

Oh, what the fuck?

The disappointment is palpable. This feeling, of looking in a mirror and seeing *that* staring back at me? It makes me want to abort this stupid session immediately. Shut it down, run from the room. Scream. Drink. Get high. Anything but sit here with this *feeling.*

Part of me can't believe it.

In the back of my mind, I know my breakdown had affected me. And I was subconsciously hoping it hadn't altered me permanently. But now, seeing that it actually *had* was soul crushing. This is me now? This is who I am at my core?

What happened to my theory that my true self is the one that created all of the others? My other selves were there before my breakdown. He wasn't around then to make them. This Little Me couldn't have created them. He can barely function on his own, much less manufacture personas stronger than he is. Maybe that was another self? One I can't see anymore? Or is it the same self, only now changed?

I'm getting confused. And frustrated. It's getting harder and harder to concentrate on my breathing. But I try.

In, out… In, out…

Something inside me says to keep looking. So I calm myself down and redouble efforts to focus on my breathing.

In, out… In, out…

After several moments, I start to feel something else.

Strength.

This strength overcomes the anxiety the Little Me image is causing. It simultaneously surrounds and fills me. I can feel my chest swell. Slowly, but surely, I start to feel stronger. And it feels amazing.

It's so fucking *strange*. I've really never felt this in tune with myself, with my thoughts before. It's like something comes up and I react to it, deep inside, viscerally. And in the *truest* definition of the word, which means "relating to deep inward feelings rather than to the intellect." I get a notion—nervousness, fear, strength—and it's like my soul or my mind or whatever confirms it.

Like with the image of Little Me, I try to illustrate what I'm feeling. I picture vines growing around the sad little character's feet. The vines are made of iron. (I "draw" them in bronze, for some reason. But the *feeling* is one of iron.) Bronze-colored vines curl and extend from below the character. Bronze leaves appear, bronze roses bloom on the vines. I don't know why this is what I'm dreaming up, but this is exactly what it feels like. It's as if my mind is assigning appropriate visuals to these sensations. I have a vivid imagination, I'll admit that. But this? This is something *weird*. I'm a little freaked out and a little amazed by it. Almost like it's not me doing it at all.

But there's this part of me, a rational part, that just can't bring these two images together. Fear. Strength. How can they be paired? It doesn't make any sense to me.

Then, from out of nowhere:

Splitting: the failure in a person's thinking to bring together the dichotomy of both positive and negative qualities of the self and others into a cohesive, realistic whole.

Is that what I'm doing? So what does that mean? That these two disparate feelings can co-exist?

I remember where I'm sitting: in a black-and-white room. Suddenly I remember a question Thomas asked me years ago in therapy.

Why can't it be both?

Yes. Why *can't* it be both?

Why couldn't I be both a frightened little man and a strong, brave force? What if I'm like a black-and-white room? What if that's my duality? And together they make up my cohesive, realistic whole? Just like this room is comprised of two opposites. Cut the space down the middle, you've got two different halves. But together? They're one.

In, out… In, out…

I remain where I am. I stay with these feelings. I try to see behind them. It doesn't feel like there's anything hiding. This *feels* like me, if I have to admit it. My heart seems to confirm it. It seems to fit.

So I do. I admit it.

Gradually, as I accept it, the more this real me crystallizes.

Yes.

It's entirely possible: I am the man who's afraid of the dark *but I'm also the man who is strong enough to crawl out of it.*

I'm someone who feels small. *But someone who also has the will to attempt great things.*

I'm frail. Yet at times *my backbone is made of solid steel.*

I'm nervous. But also *in possession of true grit.*

Maybe I approach the day full of caution. But I leave the house *filled with certainty and hope.*

The answers may frighten me. *But, goddammit, I'm brave enough to ask the questions.*

I have been utterly changed by circumstances. But *the evolution of Me is a miracle to behold.*

I'm not who I once was, I'm the next generation of Me.

With each thought, I can feel the two sides coming together. The fear is encircled by strength. Fear begins to ebb. And I start to feel this *confidence.*

I am peasant and king. I am an entire kingdom.

I am the coming storm and the brighter day.

I am all these contradictions. I am a janus. Two faces. I *am* the black-and-white room. I am two sides of the same coin. And what a currency!

I have been here for decades. Yet I am something entirely new.

What is my real self?

My real self is an ever-shifting entity. My real self is in constant flux, reacting and adapting to my environment. This is who I am now.

Or not?

Maybe I'm fooling myself and this dual man is just another alias. Maybe the real me is someone unknowable. A person only God knows. In the end, what does it matter? Because this is the real me now, the only one I know. And seeing who I am—for the better, for the worse—gives me not only a better understanding of who I am in the cosmos but a greater respect for myself as a whole.

And I see I was wrong. I'm not the subtraction of all my other selves, I am their summation. It's like light going through a prism. The white light doesn't look anything like the multi-colored beams that exit the glass. Yet all their colors together *are* the white light. And just like all these colors combined are a white light, so all my selves combine to create a unique Me, a singular being.

I take a step back, take it all in.

It *worked.*

This crazy plan I came up with…it actually worked.

Suddenly, a sense of caution rises up.

Okay, fine. Test it. See if this holds up.

I continue to sit with these feelings, this revelation. And, yes, it resonates. It feels like truth.

If I have to be honest, I did hope that, at my center, I would arrive at some kind of Thor character looking back at me. That I'd strip away all the aliases and I'd be standing there looking at Chris Hemsworth. But that's not what was there at all. Am I disappointed I didn't find some demigod at my core? Yes, a little. But I didn't find an ordinary man there, either. I found an extraordinary one. One with faults and flaws but with a resolve, a strength, and a tenacity I hadn't really counted on. One who may be even stronger *because* of his fearful side.

Slowly, I take notice of my face: I've been smiling for several minutes now. A stupid, ear-to-ear grin. An idiot grin. And I feel…

I feel *good.*

I remain seated a little while longer. Part of me doesn't want to open my eyes. I'm in a happy place. Why leave here?

Because I've been sitting here for God knows how long and all things have to come to an end. I make a quick, silent prayer to remember this all. To never forget this feeling and what's transpired here.

Gently, I open my eyes.

They've been closed so long, it takes a few seconds for them to adjust to the light. But when they do, I find myself looking at the exact point where the black side of the room meets the white side of the room. And I'm in the middle.

Perfectly, finally balanced.

AFTERGLOW

My Self

Five Months Later

ONE THOUSAND FIVE HUNDRED SEVENTEEN CALORIES. THAT'S ALL I'm allowed to consume.

I've never been on a diet this strict in my life. I've never needed to. But now I'm soft around the middle. I haven't worked out in over four years. I have a gut. And I'm sick of it.

Initially, I estimated that if I kept up this low-caloric pace, I'd lose a pound a week. If I exercise daily, I might bump that up to two. That means it would take a couple of months to work off this midsection.

Well, I didn't lose a pound.

I slimmed a whole five pounds off in just a week!

Fred told me that most of the weight worked off in the first week of dieting is water weight (bummer), and while it's hard to believe I'm toting around that much extra liquid, five pounds is five pounds and I'm stoked.

But it's a few months after this illustrious start and I've had my share of cheat days, cheat weeks, and backslides, so things have evened out since their gangbuster beginning. But I'm still doing it. Still losing a little bit of weight, still biking an hour a day, still working out four days a week. Now I've settled into a routine, and frankly, it feels good.

I use this handy calorie calculator that subtracts from my base calorie count of 1,517 with each food I eat, then adds some allowed calories with each exercise I do. (MyPlate by Livestrong. It's pretty great.) I've started living like steamed broccoli with a squeeze of lemon is an actual meal, and shocker, I really kind of like it.

My mental state is incalculably better. I have days where I'm a little bummed, but I can't call it depression. Not to the extent it was, anyway. Still, I know depression is a disease I suffer from. And I have to live with that.

I've learned that Little Me still likes to keep his shaky hand on the wheel. I know now that my initial response to just about anything is going to be fear-based. It's just the way I am now. My job is to counter that fear with bravery, a little self-talk, and go forward despite my fear. It's weird being this attuned to my own internal rhythms. In a way, it feels ridiculous that I have to have a mini come-to-Jesus with myself over just about every single thing I do. But it also feels empowering. I understand that I went through a trauma and I have some aftereffects from it. I can't change that. I wish I could, but I can't. All I can do is change my response to it.

I do live with the knowledge that RA could return and throw a monkey wrench into this whole machine. But I keep taking my meds and keep counting on them to work. My body, the one that once turned against me, has been chemically—and now mentally—beaten into submission. I'm running this show.

I don't feel like a butterfly or anything. Just a sober regard for the way things are. And a thankfulness they're so much better than they were. There's a strength to knowing who I am, the way I'm wired. As difficult or as uncomfortable as it may be, I actually work through my feelings without this desire to use sex or drugs or any other kind of distraction to avoid dealing with them. Yes, there's the initial fight-or-flight response. That rush of terror, that flush of adrenalin is still aggravatingly typical. But my response is always fight. This is new. And welcome.

My whole self-experiment worked and it worked better than I ever anticipated. I came up with a plan to find myself, succeeded in doing so, and came out the other side a stronger, more balanced person. It seems like years ago that it happened, even though it's only been a few months.

I miss my therapist, but I'm living without one. I know one is there if I ever feel the need to process or analyze or simply just talk about it to someone. But I've also realized my friends can fill this need quite capably when it arises. There's something beautiful about being honest with those you love. After decades of showing only fractions of myself to them, it's quite liberating knowing your facing people with your whole face. It's funny, the times I question a feeling, I've sometimes asked a friend about it. "Does everyone feel this way?" I'll ask. And, without fail, they always say, "I do." There's strength in numbers. And I feel better knowing I'm not in this alone.

I keep taking my psych meds. When I was crazy (sorry, Thomas, but it's still a word that works for me), I would go into a daily panic when I took my pills. There were so many, and when my supply started to diminish, anxiety would seize me. I'd freak out about what day to order them, wondering if I'd be told it's too early for the insurance or it's too late for the pharmacy and they wouldn't be able to fill them in time. Now I take the pills without any drama or stress. It's just something I have to do now that I didn't have to do years ago. I've made my peace with it. My brain chemistry has been altered. The medications bring back an equilibrium. Again, balance is achieved.

I do think back to those dark times. It's like I'm at a multiplex and there's this very dark, very discouraging, very depressing movie playing there. I'm aware of it. I even know the show times. But I don't buy a ticket. I've seen that show before and once was enough.

My faith has returned to a simpler time. Like when I was a child, I say my prayers every night. While I turn to God multiple times throughout the day, I know our time at night is set and I look forward to it. It's a standing date and I know that no matter what my day is like, I'll always have time with Someone I honestly love and Who loves me furiously. And Who knows me. For whatever reason, He allowed me to go through fucking hell. Miraculously, I came through it. Am I better for it? That's debatable. But it's getting harder and harder to remember what I was like, who I was before. I wouldn't want to go through it again, that's for damn sure. But I have a healthy respect for myself for surviving it the one time I had to.

I still, sadly, don't take as much pleasure in music as I once did. Although I did have one Saturday there where I rediscovered *The Colour and The Shape* and *really* got into it. I even sang (or screamed) along. Don't know if it's just the Foo Fighters that have regained some kind of magic power. I didn't listen to anything else that day. But hopefully the next time I listen to music, that same feeling of joy will come over me. Maybe I'll even get chills like I once did.

I am strangely affected by television. So much so that when something bad happens to a character, I go through it with them, with almost as much intensity as if it is happening to me. It's very weird and has definitely affected my entertainment choices. Maybe I'm just more empathetic now, although inappropriately so.

It's also a disappointment that the whole experience changed me physically. Years of sobbing having swollen and shrunk the skin beneath my eyes so many times that I don't have bags, I have a cargo bay full of luggage. I look like someone twenty years older. I comfort myself by telling myself I look really good from the neck down. But I'd be lying if I said it didn't ding my confidence a little bit. But considering what I went through, it's a little surprising this is the only visible residual effect. Seriously, I almost expect stigmata.

I've changed my name to match my new self. No more bullshit about a *ph* or a *v*. I spell it with a 7 now. This gets me approving head bobs from the baristas at Starbucks. That's kinda cool. I feel like a rapper. Not really. But I do feel like me. A new me. The name change is just a nice symbol of that. And every time I write my name down, it reminds me to be my whole self, my authentic self.

The selves I identified still occasionally show up, and it's nice to see they still have their old traits and strengths. The darker ones show up less and less, and when they do assert themselves, I'm able to regain control pretty much as soon as I feel their mask slipping over my eyes. The Fool still shows up more than I'd like, but we have a somewhat easy peace. I feel more and more like a Survivor every day. The Punisher knows he's not welcome at any time. He backs off with a quick, sharp warning. And the others play their parts.

I've even noticed the creation of a new alias or two. So I have a couple more than when I first started this little adventure. Author is one new alias I'm quite proud of.

At the beginning of this book, I asked you who you were.

I doubt any of you filled a goldfish bowl with slips of paper. But I do recommend the method.

Find a bowl. Think about all the people you are. Write them down. Put them in the bowl. Take them out. Look at them. Each one really does have a story. If that doesn't work for you, do it in reverse. Think of the stories first. They'll tell you which self is behind it. Then put them aside. Take a good, long look at what's left.

If you still can't see, ask God to reveal your true self to you. I promise, He's not the asshole He can appear to be. I know there's a lot of evidence that suggests otherwise, but there are plenty of places and situations where His good qualities can't be ignored. All you have to do is look at a penguin to see the Guy has one hell of an imagination. That's something. And He made you, so how bad could He be? All I can tell you is that when I went looking for Him, He was surprisingly easy to find. My take: if you need help divining your true self, a little divinity couldn't hurt.

I didn't have a clue if it would work or not. Maybe I am pretty smart. Maybe I'm just gullible. Who's to say? In the end, it did what it was supposed to. When I set all my aliases aside, what I was able to see was the real me. Not a version. Not a portion. But Me, who and what I am. My life is inestimably better now that I know that. I know my strengths and my weaknesses. I know *me*. Some days, I even catch myself liking him.

Bottom line, I don't think I've ever felt so *myself*, never felt more centered in my life. Maybe this book helped you feel the same way. Or maybe the bowl will. In any case, I hope you're maybe a little happier than when we started. I mean that.

And that's the real me talking. Not an alias.

Although that wouldn't be a bad thing if one of them were speaking for me. I've gotten to know them quite well. They're a pretty great group of guys.

If I do say so.

My self.

ACKNOWLEDGEMENTS

I'd like to thank Janice Stensrude for her invaluable gaze, Greg Jeu for bone-throwing, Shane Price for stashing my shit, Drs. Crofoot, Valicek, Kapoor, Wilkes, and especially Clark for putting the care in healthcare, my chemical brothers and sisters at the Northwest Pharmacy, Lindsay Peyton for the kiss and everything after, Thomas Owsley for the breadcrumbs, every Ghost Stories fan for telling me what I desperately needed to hear, Aggie for the pick-me-ups, Sam & Eric, they're/their music to my ears, Louis Haba for making me feel right at home, Carol Miller for the home stretch, all the early readers for your generosity, Gigi Welch and everyone with the Go Fund Me campaign for lifting me up when I was down, Jeffery Burnett for ten terrific years, Lily for giving me sheer joy, and especially Sam and Zoe for making me so proud to be and very glad I'm their dad.

Thank you for reading *The Last Alias*. If you would, post your review on Amazon. I'd love to know what you thought.

And feel free to get at me via my website www.ste7enfoster.com, or find me on Insta (ste7en_foster), Twitter (@ste7enfoster), or Facebook (foster.steven).